Journey Through the
MENTAL ILLNESS MAZE

How Families Find
Hope and Acceptance

MARJORIE SCHAFFER

ISBN-13: 978-0-578-86666-6

Cover and Interior design done by Tami Boyce (www.tamiboyce.com)

DEDICATION

*To my daughter, Sarah, who taught me about
what it means to live with a mental illness day to day.
She is courageous and resilient in finding her way to recovery.*

TABLE OF CONTENTS

PREFACE

Mental illness touches most everyone at some point. Each year, one in five adults experiences a mental health condition. Mental health conditions affect an individual's moods and thinking beyond the ups and downs that often take place in life. Many of us have a family member, friend, peer, co-worker, or neighbor who has experienced a mental health condition that affects their ability to manage daily life.

I have my own story. My daughter has lived with bipolar disorder for 25 years, and throughout these years I experienced frustration, sadness, anger, disappointment, hope, and finally acceptance as I struggled to find a way through the maze of programs and services in mental healthcare. My story inspired me to conduct a study to seek the stories of others—parents, partners, siblings, and adult children who were also finding their path as they persevered to help their relative. The findings of my study form the basis of this book.

Although having a family member living with bipolar disorder was a requirement for the study, many participants reported a variety of diagnoses and changing diagnoses throughout their relative's treatment experiences. Additional diagnoses included depression, anxiety, panic attacks, personality disorder, schizoaffective disorder, and an eating disorder.

In the study, I interviewed 20 family members (five parents, five partners, five siblings, and five adult children), all who have faced the challenge of helping a relative manage symptoms of mental illness. I asked questions about the meaning of their experiences. How did they cope? What were their sources of strength and support? How was the mental healthcare system helpful or not helpful? What did they learn about themselves?

The experiences of others help us understand our own story and show us how we can make it a better one. Sometimes we face guilt, self-blame, and shame when confronting the reality of a relative's mental illness. We learn that mental illness is no one's fault, and we discover that we are not alone in the struggle to assist our relative. This book is a guide for family members who are searching for answers to help their relative find stability and well-being while living with a mental illness. As you read, you'll find examples and strategies that will expand your understanding of how to balance compassion for your relative with your own health and well-being.

My life experiences prepared me to write this book. As a parent of an adult daughter who lives with bipolar disorder, I have learned how to navigate a complex mental healthcare system. I volunteer for the National Alliance on Mental Illness (NAMI) as a co-teacher for the Family-to-Family class and serve on the Hennepin County Adult Mental Health Advisory Council in Minnesota. My nursing career helped me develop expertise in mental healthcare settings; I have worked as a psychiatric nurse on inpatient child, adolescent, and young adult mental health units. In addition, my 31 years as a nursing professor at Bethel University in St. Paul, Minnesota, provided me with clinical experience in public health nursing—where

I encountered families facing mental health challenges—as well as the opportunity to cultivate expertise in qualitative research design.

The Bethel University Institutional Review Board approved my study, and the Chi-at-Large Chapter of Sigma Theta Tau International Honor Society of Nursing funded my research, enabling me to provide a small stipend to participants. In order to find family members to join the study, I first emailed letters of invitation to contacts from professional groups and asked them to forward my invitation to potential participants. NAMI Minnesota published a short article about my study in its newsletter, resulting in family members contacting me about participating. I interviewed participants in local library meeting rooms, at private workplace offices, and at their homes. All participant names have been changed to protect confidentiality.

The family members I interviewed expressed gratitude for the opportunity to tell their stories. They honestly and poignantly shared their experiences. They expressed many emotions—sadness, grief, anger, frustration, and disappointment. They described how difficult times led to new understanding and growth—developing compassion for others, learning self-care, and finding strengths in themselves and their relative. The participants in my study courageously searched for knowledge, understanding, and resources to help their relative. Their wisdom provides insight for family members about the importance of taking care of your own needs, setting boundaries, and letting go when the burden becomes too great. You can find the participants' complete stories at my website: **www.familybipolarstories.com.**

ACCEPTANCE

I didn't know. I couldn't understand.
My adult child's mind. Filled with wild ideas, not possible.
Not sleeping. Impulsive. Brought to the hospital.
Why? What could I hope for?

For me, sadness. Trying to help.
The world, full of danger.
Scared for my child. What could I do?
I needed help. How?

I found others. Similar experiences.
They grieved the loss of someone no longer the same.
They hurt. They cared.
I learned about expectations. How do I let go?

I found helpers. Some wonderful. Others not so great.
What can I do when my adult child does not take her medications?
I reel with her manic episodes and hospitalizations.
How do I get through?

Learning about advocacy.
Teaching and supporting others.
Speaking about mental illness. I find my voice.
I write the stories. I do what I can. I am getting through.

Help makes a difference.
Psychiatrists, nurses, social workers, case managers.
Housing subsidy, Social Security disability, recovery programs.
Living independently with support. Right now, stability for my child. I am grateful.

I see hope. I see recovery.
My adult child, resilient. Choosing her life experiences.
The future, uncertain.
For me, uncertainty, but also acceptance.

—Marjorie A. Schaffer

Chapter 1

INTRODUCTION

Have you gone down fruitless pathways, encountered roadblocks, and felt baffled or trapped in the search for quality treatment and services for a loved one living with a mental illness? The metaphor of a maze aptly portrays this complex journey. What pathways or choices are best? Which will lead to recovery? What outcome can we expect to reach? How do we take care of ourselves during what is often a stressful and overwhelming journey?

The voices of family members who tell stories of their routes through the mental illness maze give us insight and tools for our own journey. Many others have experienced a similar journey and prevailed in the dual purpose of boosting their own well-being and supporting a loved one. The chapters in this book are derived from both the wisdom of family members who are traveling through the mental illness maze and the advice of experts who endeavor to provide healing strategies.

To find your way to hope and acceptance as you confront mental illness in family life, explore the strategies that 20 study participants shared in their stories. They embarked on a journey to learn about mental illness, leaving shame and blame behind them. They discovered that patience and time were needed to learn about resources and help their loved one find effective treatment. Discovery of realistic expectations, learning how to reframe family relationships, and developing empathy facilitated their journeys through the mental illness maze. These study participants formed social support networks that helped them navigate the maze more quickly and gained resilience to continue moving forward. They found realistic hope, learned how to support recovery for their relative and for themselves, and embraced self-care strategies to address their own well-being. As they managed their journeys through the maze, study participants shared their stories of advocating for better mental health services for their relative and their community.

WHO ARE THE FAMILY MEMBERS IN THE STORIES?

The experiences of all 20 participants (five parents, five partners, five siblings, and five adult children) are featured in the following chapters. Most chapters present the stories of two or three participants in each family member group. You will find a summary of each family member group in Appendix B. Here is a brief description of each participant.

Parents

#1. Joann, mother of young adult son, Jacob. Joann moved from confusion about what was happening with her son to becoming educated and engaging in advocacy.

#2. Connie, mother of young adult daughter, Naomi. As she struggled to understand Naomi's actions, Connie concluded, "Her brain got hijacked." She learned the language needed to effectively navigate confusing systems of care and found the resources needed to support Naomi's recovery.

#3. Sharon, mother of young adult daughter, Gabrielle. Sharon walked alongside her daughter through hospitalizations and toward independence, notably coaching her on managing a budget.

#4. Anita, mother of two adopted young adult daughters, Serena and Nina, who both developed symptoms of mental illness. Anita coped by calling on her strengths and accepting her situation. She noted, "It is what it is."

#5. Elaine, mother of middle-aged daughter, Terry. Elaine focused on positive affirmation for herself and her daughter. She engaged in teaching healing strategies to others and explained, "I have a purpose."

Partners/Spouses

#1. Frank, husband of Gloria. Now in his 70s, Frank supported Gloria throughout their marriage. He relied on his faith in God and on support groups to help him persevere throughout difficult situations in family life. Frank said his motto for helping Gloria to manage her mental illness was "Be firm and be very kind."

#2. Jim, husband of Monica. Jim learned to balance Monica's needs with his own. Given financial challenges stemming from his wife's inability to work, Jim focused on appreciating the benefits of a simpler life. He recognized his self-growth, noting, "You learn to have patience."

#3. Brenda, wife of Don. Brenda experienced chaos and significant life disruptions when her husband's manic symptoms escalated. She focused on Don's perspectives and developed compassion for what he experiences on a daily basis, and she engaged in the self-care activities that keep her going. She summed up her approach by saying, "We make the best of today and we go forward."

#4. Holly, wife of Ron. Ron left their marriage and later died in a car accident. Holly acknowledged the challenging situations she encountered with Ron, saying, "I was on a roller coaster."

#5. Marta, partner to Tim. Marta decided to separate from Tim, whose behavior threatened her and their children. She developed confidence in her ability to adjust to her new situation as a single parent of two children. She summed up her approach as "I take it one day at a time."

Siblings

#1. Katie, older sister of Kevin. Kevin first exhibited symptoms of mental illness in his late teens. For years, she acted as a martyr in attempting to help her brother and support her mother. Now, Katie has developed a healthy realism about the limitations that mental illness symptoms bring to her brother's life. She learned to focus her energy on meeting needs for herself, her husband, and their two children.

#2. Dick, brother of Stuart. Dick expressed ambivalence about the demands on his life resulting from the mental illness symptoms experienced by his brother. Although Dick asked, "Why me?" he took on responsibility to support his brother and became an advocate by teaching classes to other family members whose relatives live with a mental illness.

#3. Heather, sister of Brad and wife of Scott. Both men live with bipolar disorder. Brad's symptoms limit his ability to live independently, in contrast to Scott, who manages his symptoms effectively through medication and building structure into his life. To manage her difficult emotions connected with encountering mental illness in family life, Heather writes in journals and advocates in the community for the needs of individuals who live with a mental illness.

#4. Janet, sister of David. David developed symptoms when Janet was away at college. As their mother aged, Janet and her sister stepped up their supportive actions for David, who continues to live independently. Janet communicates a strong message of acceptance: "Let people be who they are."

#5. Carmen, sister of Lily. As a teenager, Carmen was confused by what happened to Lily, who attempted suicide at age 19. When Lily needed hospitalization years later, Carmen rushed to her side to accompany her through healing and recovery. She applauds Lily's life accomplishments, proclaiming, "I'm proud of her."

Adult Children

#1. Mark, son of Gene. When Mark was 10, his father was hospi-
talized for threatening behavior, and after a brief return home,
left permanently for ongoing treatment and care. As a teenager, Mark struggled without a reliable father figure in his life.
He commented, "I didn't know if I was okay." As an adult,
Mark sought therapy and built a satisfying life with his wife and
young daughter that does not include his father.

#2. Jessica, daughter of Diane. As a teenager, Jessica first learned
about her mother's symptoms of mental illness. Diane sought
family therapy and managed her symptoms through medication
and building structure into her life to reduce stress. Jessica focuses on her mother's accomplishments and views her as "just
my mom."

#3. Sam, son of Miriam. At age 17, Sam discovered his mother fol-
lowing her completed suicide. He remembers thinking he was
to blame for her death. Earlier in his childhood, when his father
traveled for work, Sam took on responsibility for monitoring
his mother's medication. Now he channels his past experiences
into serving as a social worker to help individuals access mental
health services.

#4. Melanie, daughter of Gordon. Melanie experienced chaos in
family life stemming from her father's symptoms and her younger brother Paul's disruptive behavior, later attributed to early
onset bipolar disorder. She explained, "I survived by being quiet and good." Melanie observed that her experiences with her

father and brother helped her become more understanding of the experiences of others.

#5. Abby, daughter of Mandy. Mandy, who lives with bipolar disorder, exhibited scary symptoms of mental illness following treatment for cancer. Abby's family experienced the trauma of Mandy's car accident and disappearance, followed by a series of hospitalizations that failed to result in effective treatment. Abby strove to balance supporting her mother with managing her own family and work responsibilities.

FINDING YOUR WAY THROUGH THE MAZE

What outcomes result from navigating the maze thrust upon you when mental illness occurs in family life? While most family members featured in this book found effective strategies for supporting their relative, others needed to distance themselves from relationships that threatened their own well-being. However, all achieved significant self-growth and expanded their repertoire of coping strategies.

Although you may find yourself in the maze once again when your family member experiences escalating symptoms or mental health crises, you will gain the confidence and knowledge needed to navigate future maze journeys.

Chapter 2

THE COMPLEXITY OF MENTAL HEALTH CONDITIONS

Try to read everything you can about the person's illness.
Be educated. For me, knowledge is power.
(Katie, study participant)

Although you may be determined to learn about mental illness diagnoses and treatment, it is not easy to find your way through the vast maze of available information. Caution is required when perusing the internet, since content may not be based on scientific evidence. Furthermore, the complexity of the mental healthcare system is often bewildering as you search for information and assistance. In this chapter, an overview of mental health conditions and a summary of treatment options will help you find your way through the maze of overwhelming information. You will learn that mental illness results from complex biological, environmental, and social factors and is no one's fault.

LEAVE BLAME AND SHAME BEHIND

Have you experienced blame for your relative's mental illness symptoms? In the past, it was common to blame the family for a relative's symptoms, and vestiges of assigning fault remain today. For example, Connie's ex-husband and a daughter blamed her for her daughter Naomi's problems. Family members brought up past suicide attempts by Connie's mother and sister.

> They told me, "Connie, you gave this to Naomi." Laura [Naomi's sister] told me, "It's your blood line; it's genetic. Thanks for putting the crazy gene in me. Now who's going to want to marry me because I have a crazy sister...There is a genetic marker and that comes from you. This is from your family. Your family is weak."

When Connie and her husband Dan joined education and support groups to help them cope, they began to understand what happened to Naomi.

> The realization that there was an illness came at different times for every member of the family, and it came in different ways. For Dan and me, it's like [Naomi's mental illness] is real. She didn't cause this. Her brain got hijacked.

Anita, whose two young adult adopted daughters both live with a mental illness, is plagued by self-doubt when she hears that parents are blamed for mental illness in their children.

> *I don't know what it's like to have biological children and have a mental illness come in. I think it's more genetic, honestly. I'm kind of sick of this feeling of shame on the part of the mother, the parent.*

The parents in my study felt shame and fear of being judged or blamed by others. Over time, with education and support, they learned that mental illness is no one's fault.

Heather realized she could not blame her brother for behavior related to his mental illness.

> *I'm trying to understand what's going on, but I'm angry that my brother is acting mean towards my parents. But I still love him; I can't blame him because he doesn't understand what he's doing.*

She sought out National Alliance on Mental Illness (NAMI) resources and recalled at first feeling ashamed when the NAMI newsletter arrived in her mailbox. Now that she has worked through her feelings of stigma and discrimination, Heather no longer feels that shame, and she participates in NAMI advocacy events.

Dick is the primary caregiver for his younger brother, Stuart, who lives with bipolar disorder. When Stuart's manic symptoms emerged at age 19, he initially refused treatment, and then the medications he received during his first hospitalization were not effective. At the time, Dick thought he shouldn't feel the shame he experienced about his brother's illness; he remembers breaking down and crying. Now, Dick is a NAMI volunteer. He co-teaches the Family-to-Family class, helping others to manage feelings of guilt and shame.

Blame had a substantial impact on the adult children in my study as they attempted to resolve childhood memories. Sam and his younger sister found out in adulthood that they had both blamed themselves for their mother's suicide. For a long time, Sam believed his mother died because she did not want him to take a job at a restaurant. He was leaving to interview for the job when he discovered his mother dead by suicide in the family garage. Twenty years later, his sister revealed she thought she caused her mother's death because she asked her mother for a puppy.

Mark's father, Gene, diagnosed as "mentally ill and dangerous," left the family home during Mark's childhood as a result of a civil commitment and hospitalization. Mark remembers that hospital staff blamed him and his mother for his father's behavior because of what Gene said about them. Gene's side of the family blamed his behavior on Mark's immediate family. When his family was blamed for everything that went wrong with Gene, Mark revealed, "It pretty much shot whatever self-esteem I had at that age into pieces. I probably didn't have real great self-esteem until my mid-20s." He explained that although he felt he was derailed from being able to become what he could have been, he also learned what he didn't want to be in life.

Sam and Mark both experienced the disappearance of a parent during childhood due to the severity of their parent's mental illness symptoms. Their experiences led to a search for identity; both resolved doubts about their ability to be successful in life. Now, as a county mental health social worker, Sam advocates for people who live with a mental illness. He estimates he has served as a caseworker for 1,000 people over the years. Mark sought therapy in adulthood, noting that therapy was not an option for him during his childhood. He is now married, is starting a family, and looks forward to enjoying life with his family. He sees a bright future for his daughter and "calm" in his family life. He has responded with self-awareness and honesty in facing the lifelong challenge of having a father who lives with a mental illness. Mark now knows he is making choices in his life that are good for him.

Discrimination Contributes to Blame and Shame

How does discrimination contribute to blame and shame? Research confirms that discrimination and stigma negatively affect the well-being of family members who support a relative living with a mental illness. Consider the difference between stigma and discrimination. Stigma occurs when someone *sees* you in a negative way because of mental illness, while discrimination occurs when someone *treats* you in a negative way because of mental illness.[1] Stigma focuses on perceptions of deficiencies or flaws, while discrimination refers to the unacceptable behavior connected to damaging beliefs about people who live with a mental illness.

Negative beliefs lead to negative stereotypes that persist over time, such as wrong beliefs that individuals living with a mental illness are unpredictable, dangerous, and incompetent.[2] Negative stereotypes include the belief that mental illness is a moral failing due to faulty character or lack of self-control, and the assumption that mental illness can be conquered by "pulling yourself up by your bootstraps."[3]

Family members may also experience the harmful effects of stigma and discrimination because of their connection with their relative.[4,5] They may be blamed for causing their relative's illness or failing to help them stick with a treatment plan. Stigma occurs when family members witness the stigma encountered by their relative, experience guilt and isolation, or are ignored by mental health-care providers. Over time, as family members internalize stigma and carry it with them, its burden damages their relationships and well-being. Family members may communicate a sense of stigma to their relative through extreme worrying and overprotection.[6] Stigma toward family members in mental healthcare settings is also a reality; more than half of family members in a survey reported experiencing stigma in interactions with mental health and social service professionals.[5]

Today, mental health advocacy organizations are putting great effort into educating the public about mental illness and reducing the stigma and discrimination that contribute to harm for persons living with a mental illness and their family members. The Mayo Clinic website explains that stigma contributes to the following harmful effects for individuals needing mental healthcare:[7]

- Reluctance to seek help, which results in delayed treatment
- Isolation due to a lack of understanding
- Reduced opportunities for employment, school, social activities, and housing
- Bullying or harassment
- Inadequate health insurance for covering treatment
- The belief that the situation cannot be improved

We each need to do our part to reduce stigma and discrimination related to mental illness. The following actions counteract both in our community and society:[1,7,8]

- Learn facts about mental illness and share them.

- Get to know people who have personal experiences with mental illness and focus on the person rather than the illness.
- Treat all people with respect and dignity; avoid judging and labelling.
- Use person-first language—for example, say "a person living with bipolar disorder" rather than "a bipolar person."
- Challenge or confront inaccurate or stereotypical comments about mental illness.
- Resist letting harmful comments influence your own self-talk.
- Share your own experience as someone who lives with a mental illness or as a family member.
- Develop resilience, a protective factor that reduces the harmful effects of stigma and discrimination.

WHAT CAUSES MENTAL ILLNESS?

Some mental health conditions, including schizophrenia and bipolar disorder, are linked to brain structural and functional abnormalities apparent in imaging scans or a postmortem examination. However, other conditions, such as depression and anxiety, appear to be associated with a broader interplay of genetic, biological, environmental, and social factors.[9,10] Risk factors include a history of mental illness in a blood relative (particularly a parent or sibling), stressful life circumstances, chronic medical conditions, a traumatic brain injury, traumatic experiences, alcohol or recreational drug use, a history of childhood abuse or neglect, and exposure to toxins.[12,16]

Family members in my study searched for causes of their relative's mental illness. Many explained they have other family members who currently live with a mental illness or have in the past. Several reported that their relative experienced one or more head injuries. Janet believes her brother David's experience of emotional trauma during childhood triggered his bipolar disorder. As a young boy, David went to the family's Catholic church to learn about being an altar boy. Janet's mother reported that he "came back home, was very upset, and said, 'I will never go there ever again.'" The priest who came to their house during David's first manic episode was later found to be a sexual predator. Janet wondered what had happened to her brother.

> *I'm thinking, what kind of trauma did my brother maybe have when he was a little boy that never got talked about that he internalized? Could it have been a factor behind all this?...My mother [a school nurse] felt that when he was young, in elementary school, he needed mental health [services], but my father didn't think that was necessary, so they didn't go forward.*

One way to think about the relationship between genetics and environment is that genetics predisposes one to the development of mental illness, while stress in one's environment pulls the trigger.

OVERVIEW OF MENTAL HEALTH CONDITIONS

Mental illness affects emotions, thoughts, and behaviors. The National Institute of Mental Health[11] names two categories of mental health conditions: 1) any mental illness and 2) serious mental illness.

- Any mental illness (AMI) ranges from no impairment to mild, moderate, or severe impairment; it is estimated that 18.9% of adults in the United States lived with AMI in 2017.

- Serious mental illness (SMI), as a subset of AMI, results in serious impairment that interferes with life activities; it is estimated that 4.5% of adults in the United States lived with SMI in 2017.

Signs and symptoms of mental illness often cut across various diagnoses, which increases the difficulty of determining an accurate diagnosis. This difficulty may lead to differing opinions and changing diagnoses over time. The Mayo Clinic website lists the following signs and symptoms that may occur in mental illness:[12]

- Feeling sad or down
- Confused thinking or reduced ability to concentrate
- Excessive fears or worries, or extreme feelings of guilt
- Extreme mood changes of highs and lows
- Withdrawal from friends and activities
- Significant tiredness, low energy, or problems sleeping
- Detachment from reality (delusions), paranoia, or hallucinations
- Inability to cope with daily problems or stress
- Trouble understanding and relating to situations and people
- Problems with alcohol or drug use
- Major changes in eating habits
- Sex drive changes
- Excessive anger, hostility, or violence
- Suicidal thinking

Diagnosis of a mental illness is based on both observation by others and reports from the person experiencing symptoms. Healthcare providers look for patterns of behavior that are typical for a specific diagnosis as identified in the *Diagnostic and Statistical Manual of Mental Disorders* (*DSM*). The *DSM* is a guidebook for mental health professionals that lists symptoms and diagnostic criteria for mental health conditions; it is periodically updated by the American Psychological Association to reflect new research findings and added diagnoses. It is important to rule out any causes of symptoms of mental illness resulting from medical conditions that affect brain chemistry.

The severity of mental illness is an important factor in determining what treatment will be helpful. The Mental Health America website identifies four stages of mental health conditions:[13]

1. *Mild symptoms and warning signs:* Early symptoms of mental illness are apparent, although a person continues to function at home, work, or school.
2. *Increase in frequency and severity of symptoms:* Symptoms interfere with life activities and roles, indicating that something is wrong.
3. *Symptoms become worse with recurring episodes:* Serious disruptions in life activities and roles occur.
4. *Symptoms are severe, persistent, and threaten life:* Prolonged persistent symptoms and impairment often contribute to other health conditions and result in unemployment, hospitalization, homelessness, or incarceration. On average, untreated mental illnesses contribute to a lifespan reduction of 25 years.

Although symptoms are used to determine a diagnosis, making the determination may necessitate several episodes of symptom patterns. This complexity can lead to a delay in diagnosis and effective treatment. The following list[14] identifies the most common diagnoses; you will find a complete list of mental health conditions in the *DSM*.

- **Anxiety disorders:** overwhelming anxiety that negatively impacts a person's life
- **Attention deficit hyperactivity disorder:** a developmental disorder featuring problems with attention, hyperactivity, or impulsivity
- **Autism:** a developmental disorder that affects the ability to socialize and communicate with others (also known as autism spectrum disorder)
- **Bipolar disorder:** dramatic changes in mood, from high to low, that affect one's activity level and ability to think clearly
- **Borderline personality disorder:** a pattern of instability or dysregulation in moods, self-image, and interpersonal relationships that disrupt daily life; symptoms may include impulsivity and self-harm
- **Depression:** feelings of sadness and loss of interest in life that negatively impact functioning in work, school, family, and social settings over a minimum of two weeks[15]
- **Dissociative disorders:** disruption of memory and self-perception
- **Early psychosis and psychosis:** disruption of thoughts that affect accurate perceptions of reality (psychosis may occur in bipolar disorder, schizophrenia, and schizoaffective disorder)
- **Eating disorders:** preoccupation with food and weight that makes it difficult to manage a healthy life
- **Obsessive-compulsive disorder:** repetitive, intrusive, and irrational thoughts that lead to the compulsion to perform certain actions repeatedly
- **Posttraumatic stress disorder:** long-term cognitive, emotional, and behavioral symptoms following a traumatic event such as an accident, a natural disaster, assault, or military combat

- **Schizoaffective disorder:** combination of symptoms characteristic of schizophrenia (hallucinations or delusions) and a mood disorder (depressive or manic episodes)
- **Schizophrenia:** loss of touch with reality exhibited through hallucinations, delusions, and disordered thinking and behavior

Mental illness occurs on a continuum, meaning there is a large range of symptom severity across mental health conditions. Some individuals may experience mild symptoms that family and friends attribute to personality characteristics, while others may develop severe symptoms that diminish their ability to function in family and community life. Also, individuals who receive a mental illness diagnosis as an adult may have exhibited characteristics and behaviors as a child that family members view as having been indicative of future development of symptoms.

Although all family members in my study reported that their relative was diagnosed with bipolar disorder, six of the 20 participants identified that their relative had additional diagnoses including depression, schizoaffective disorder, anxiety, and an eating disorder. It is important to note that when depressive symptoms occur first, providers may miss a diagnosis of bipolar disorder if a manic episode has not yet been observed. Some participants' relatives also exhibited a substance abuse disorder—frequent and repeated use of alcohol and/or drugs that contributes to health problems, disability, and the ability to carry out one's responsibilities.[16] Substance abuse may be a contributing factor to mental illness symptoms, or mental illness may contribute to substance abuse behavior.

Where Do I Find Good Information?

You can learn more about mental health conditions through credible resources, such as government sites, respected healthcare systems, and mental health organizations. Avoid general Google searches that may lead you to inaccurate, biased information. Some of the best resources for accurate information on mental health conditions are:

- American Psychiatric Association
- https://www.psychiatry.org/patients-families

- Centers for Disease Control and Prevention
- https://www.cdc.gov/mentalhealth/learn

- Mayo Clinic
- https://www.mayoclinic.org/diseases-conditions/mental-illness/symptoms-causes/syc-20374968

- National Alliance on Mental Health
- https://www.nami.org/Learn-MoreMental-Health-Conditions

- National Institute of Mental Health
- https://www.nimh.nih.gov/health/topics/index.shtml

RESOURCES, INTERVENTIONS, AND COMMUNITY SUPPORT

We need others to help us as we support and care for a relative living with a mental illness. Trying do this on our own will only lead to emotional and physical exhaustion, depleting us of our ability to remain compassionate toward our relative's challenges. However, when we first confront the reality of their diagnosis, there is so much we do not know about treatment resources—availability, services, eligibility requirements, and cost. The learning curve can seem extremely daunting. There are both government resources and non-profit community resources, and funding for these resources may come and go, changing what services are offered. Also, available resources vary greatly across states, often depending on the state's political environment and willingness to fund mental health programs. A brief overview of resources and interventions to support people who live with mental illness and their families is presented here.

Mental Health Crisis Response Teams

Where available, crisis teams of mental health professionals will respond to a request for help when someone is experiencing a mental health crisis. The team responds to phone calls and can go to the location of the crisis and evaluate the individual. Referral to other professionals and follow-up services, including hospitalization, is provided if needed. Availability is usually 24/7. Call a crisis team if your family member is suicidal, psychotic, exhibiting out of control behavior, or threatening to harm themselves or others. Other options for help in a crisis include national and local suicide prevention hotlines.

Hospitals

When individuals are identified as living with a severe mental illness and are unsafe to live in the community owing to the potential for harming themselves or others, they may need hospitalization in an inpatient mental health or psychiatric unit. The goal is to stabilize the individual with a treatment and recovery plan. If they are admitted to the hospital but an inpatient psychiatric bed is not available, the individual may spend an extended time in the emergency room before being moved to a mental health unit. Some hospitals offer acute psychiatric care for emergency mental health situations. If an individual is threatening to leave the hospital and is determined to be a danger to themselves or others, an emergency hold is used to keep the person hospitalized. Depending on state laws, they may be admitted to the hospital for a minimum of 72 hours for evaluation.

In the hospital, a psychiatrist employed by the hospital supervises care; they are usually a different psychiatrist from the one who follows the individual after discharge. The hospital social worker is the "go-to" person for discharge planning and for conveying family member messages to mental health providers and staff. The Health Insurance Portability and Accountability Act of 1996 (known as HIPAA) mandates privacy rules about communication of health information, which sometimes creates a barrier for family members. To receive information about a hospitalized individual over 18, the individual must sign a release of information form that allows hospital staff and providers to communicate with specific people about the patient's status and treatment.

Individuals with a long-lasting, severe, and persistent mental illness may be hospitalized at a regional treatment center—a state-administered hospital that offers intensive mental health treatment.

First Episode Psychosis Programs

Programs for individuals with a history of a first psychotic episode are available in many states. The goal is early treatment, intended to reduce the long-term negative effects resulting from repeated episodes. These programs have a multidisciplinary approach, provide intensive early intervention, help clients and their families navigate the complex mental healthcare system, and offer education and support to individuals who live with a mental illness and their family members. Research evidence demonstrates the effectiveness of early intervention in promoting recovery and reducing the long-term negative consequences of repeated psychotic episodes.[17,18]

Civil Commitment

Family members or hospital staff may initiate a civil commitment hearing in the court system if an individual refuses treatment and is severely ill. Civil commitment is pursued to treat individuals who are unable or unwilling to voluntarily seek treatment and to protect individuals with a mental illness from harming themselves or others as a result of their symptoms. The commitment process involves several steps, including prepetition screening; filing the petition; examination by a licensed psychologist or psychiatrist; a preliminary hearing with lawyers and judge; the commitment hearing, which usually takes place in a courtroom; and the commitment decision. Family members can respond to questions from the prepetition screener and testify at the commitment trial.

A decision for commitment means the individual with mental illness is mandated to comply with treatment. Individuals who are committed may be discharged from the hospital as long as they agree to comply with treatment, but if they do not, they may be sent back to inpatient treatment. Civil commitment time periods generally range from six months to a year and may be extended depending on the individual's progress. Civil commitment rules vary across states. A stay of commitment happens when a commitment order for treatment is not executed as long as the individual meets the conditions stated in the commitment order.

Crisis Intervention Teams

Individuals with a mental illness may encounter law enforcement as a result of their symptoms and public behavior or in response to reported concerns about the individual's safety. When an individual experiences a severe psychosis, police officers may be called to respond to behaviors that are interpreted as criminal behavior. In this situation, individuals with severe psychiatric symptoms may be taken to jail. Crisis Intervention Teams (CITs), which address mental health crises, offer an alternative response. CIT-trained police officers learn from other members of law enforcement, mental health providers, and hospital emergency staff about how respond to persons in crisis. Training for police officers generally involves learning de-escalation skills. Some communities also include a mental healthcare expert on the CIT team. CIT programs reduce arrests and help individuals find needed treatment.[19] Some states offer specialty courts to address the needs of people who live with a mental illness, which may be called Mental Health Court, Drug Court, or Restorative Justice Court.

Outpatient and Day Treatment

Following discharge from the hospital, clients may be referred to aftercare programs. Clients in outpatient programs have regular appointments for therapy and medication management. Day treatment, offered a specified number of days each week, provides intensive services with the goals of improving an individual's stability and enabling them to transition from a structured setting to successful living in a community setting.

Dual Diagnosis Treatment Programs

We are seeing an increase in dual diagnosis programs, which provide concurrent treatment for substance abuse disorders and mental health conditions. Rather than separating treatment for substance abuse and mental illness, these programs are typically administered under the broad category of behavioral health.

Residential Treatment

People living with a mental illness may be referred to residential treatment for crisis management, where they can stay up to three months, or to places where they can live for a longer time period. In short-term crisis care, clients typically stay for less than a week for stabilization until another mental health program or housing becomes available. Intensive Residential Treatment Services, known as IRTS, provide mental health services in a 16-bed residential setting that focuses on managing symptoms and medication, learning coping skills, and socialization. Stays are up to three months but may be shorter if the client is stable and has a safe living situation in the community. IRTS facilities are not available in all states.

More permanent residential settings for persons living with a mental illness who need structured living situations include group homes, foster care, and assisted living.

Mental Healthcare Workers

You will find a mix of mental healthcare providers and staff in hospital and community settings. Much of mental healthcare is team-based and multidisciplinary. Care is delivered in a variety of settings, including primary care. In addition to psychiatrists, psychologists, psychiatric nurses, and social workers, you will find therapists, mental health and addiction counselors, psychiatric aids and other paraprofessionals, recovery coaches, and peer support specialists in the mental health workforce.[20] With additional training, peer support specialists, who live with a mental health condition or substance abuse disorder, use their experience to support others during recovery. Although we are seeing a greater emphasis on providing culturally appropriate mental healthcare that addresses individual beliefs and values, diversity in the mental health workforce is lacking.

Social Security Disability

Persons who are disabled because they live with a serious mental illness are eligible to receive a monthly cash payment through Social Security or Supplemental Security Income disability programs run by the Social Security Administration, an agency of the federal government. When an individual receives Social Security disability benefits, they may be eligible for other state-sponsored mental health programs. Individuals apply for benefits through the Social Security office (www.ssa.gov). Determination of disability is based on clinical evidence and examinations. The application process may take a long time and involve appeals. Individuals who receive Social Security disability benefits have the option of returning to work with a reduction or termination of benefits.

Mental Health Case Management

For people living with a serious and persistent mental illness, a case manager can coordinate referrals and services (e.g., medical, social, educational, vocational) to address mental health needs. Mental health case management is offered through a variety of community organizations that specialize in mental health services; referral typically occurs following repeated hospitalizations for mental health crises. Services are individualized and focused on supporting healthy living. Individuals must meet specific criteria for case management. There is limited availability of services, and these services vary across states.

Community Mental Health Programs

Many community organizations provide information and services to individuals living with a mental illness and their families. State and local governments often contract with nonprofit agencies to provide mental health services. Community resources for people living with a mental illness include Assertive Community Treatment (ACT) teams, supported housing, supported employment, and mental health clubhouses.

ACT teams provide intensive rehabilitative in-home services to people living with a serious mental illness who live on their own or with family or friends. These teams consist of a psychiatrist, a case manager, and a nurse for medication management. The ACT team's goals are to promote stabilization in a community setting and help the individual avoid rehospitalization.

The mental health clubhouse model provides a welcoming and caring environment in the community to support people who live with a mental illness. Services are comprehensive and address needs for employment, housing, education, friendship, and medical and psychiatric services. Mental health clubhouses help individuals know they are not alone in their recovery journey.

A variety of government and nonprofit organizations at national, state, and local levels offer education and support to people living with a mental illness and their families. They may provide both face-to-face learning opportunities and online resources. NAMI has a vast array of informational material, classes, and support groups. Its Family-to-Family class offers evidence-based education and support to family members. Co-facilitators, who also have a family member living with a mental illness, provide education on mental illnesses, medications, and side effects; teach skills in building empathy, developing coping strategies, problem-solving, and communication; and share information on helpful resources in the community. NAMI also offers a one-day Hope for Recovery class for family members as well as support groups for families and people who live with a mental health condition.

Medications

Medication, together with therapy and support programs, is an important component of the treatment plan for individuals living with a mental illness. Medications for managing symptoms affect electrochemical communication in the brain. Research is investigating how these medications work, but it is a complex and unclear process. That is why it is often difficult to find the right medication and dose that most effectively regulates symptoms. Some of the most common medications prescribed for mental illness symptoms include mood stabilizers, antipsychotics, antidepressants, and anti-anxiety medications. It is important to monitor side effects and how individuals tolerate a medication. Sometimes another medication may be prescribed to counteract side effects. For example, tremors and jerky movements (also known as tardive dyskinesia) can result from some antipsychotics.

The medications first prescribed may not be effective, since each person is unique. In the past, it could take years to identify a diagnosis and then additional years to find an effective medication. More recently, research using brain imaging is exploring how medications affect brain function, and DNA studies are available to help determine which medications are most likely to be effective for specific individuals.

Early in their illness process, persons exhibiting symptoms may not believe they are sick. Some medications take weeks to work, leading to discouragement. If the medication makes them feel better, they may believe they no longer need to take it. Or they may not like the way the medication makes them feel. If, for example, they feel slower in their thinking and less productive, they may prefer the way they felt without medication, or they may believe the medication blunts their personality.

Side effects are often a barrier to staying on a medication. A person living with a mental illness may forget to take their medication or take it inconsistently. When unhappy with a medication, an individual may not provide accurate information to their healthcare provider and family members about whether they are taking it consistently. In addition, medications may be perceived as inconvenient—for instance, if they require making additional appointments (e.g., to receive an injectable medication) or undergoing diagnostic tests to determine whether the medication is at a therapeutic level or causing a medical problem.

Medication complications are extremely common. A medication that has worked for years may stop being effective. Medications and treatment for other illnesses may change the effectiveness of psychiatric medications. Aging may also alter medication effectiveness because of changes in metabolism and interactions with other medications.

Other problems are financial and logistical. Medication may be costly, requiring individuals to sacrifice in other areas of daily living. Sometimes a health insurance company decides to stop covering a medication that has worked for someone for years, resulting in the need to take an alternative medication that may be less effective or cause more side effects. Given the psychiatrist shortage in the United States, being unable to make a timely appointment with a psychiatrist to evaluate medication complications is also a common barrier. When a medication is changed, adjustments may take time, requiring gradually tapering the dose of the previous medication and gradually increasing the new one. Finding the right medication is a complex process!

Other Treatment Options

Although in the past, treatment of mental illness often focused primarily on prescribing medications, today treatment often integrates other approaches combined with medications.

Psychotherapy; electroconvulsive therapy (ECT); self-management strategies; and spiritual approaches such as meditation, faith, and prayer also contribute to symptom management. Cognitive behavioral therapy (CBT), a form of psychotherapy, addresses thoughts that drive emotional responses—which can help certain situations become more manageable. Individuals learn to understand their stressors and triggers that lead to symptoms. Dialectical behavior therapy (DBT) is similar but more focused on building skills to help regulate emotions. DBT sessions focus on strategies for acceptance and change, including mindfulness, distress tolerance, emotional regulation, and interpersonal effectiveness.

When medications do not work, health providers may prescribe ECT, which uses electric currents to produce mild seizures during multiple sessions. ECT seems to cause changes in brain chemistry that reverse symptoms of certain mental health conditions.[21] Although ECT is now a much less traumatic treatment than in the past, temporary memory loss is a possible side effect. More recently, repetitive transcranial magnetic stimulation (TMS) has been prescribed for treatment-resistant depression. TMS is noninvasive and uses an electromagnet to stimulate nerve cells in the part of the brain that regulates mood and depression.[22]

Self-management strategies that improve brain function may enhance medication effectiveness. Self-management strategies include establishing a structured schedule and healthy routines (sleep regulation, social activities, nutritious food, exercise, pets, mindfulness, and building healthy relationships). Self-management also means avoiding excessive and harmful substances—too much caffeine, nicotine, amphetamines, alcohol, marijuana, illegal drugs, and weight-loss and energy supplements.

FAMILY MEMBER EXPERIENCES WITH MENTAL HEALTH SERVICES AND EDUCATION

What did the family members in my study learn when seeking mental health services for a relative?

They discovered that the HIPAA Privacy Rule allows family members to provide information about their relative to healthcare providers. When Joann's adult son, Jacob, was hospitalized for the first time, she wished hospital staff had informed her about HIPAA rules during her son's intake. Eventually, she discovered she could share information with staff, but they could not share information about Jacob unless he signed a release.

Family members learned about the challenges of finding competent care and needing to learn a new language about mental health. Connie explained that dealing with the legal system in mental health–related situations is a "crapshoot" and "the luck of the draw." She learned about the language she needed to use to work effectively with hospital systems and the court and became knowledgeable about the continuum of services available for people living with a mental illness. She explained,

> They're talking to you, but until you understand the language, it can feel like they're talking at you. You're under stress already. It's not an ideal time to be learning a second language on mental health and legal, yet you have to. I felt like I was running as fast as I can, like walking through Jell-O or concrete starting to harden.

Education on mental illness was—and continues to be—a key form of support for Connie. She learned to avoid buying into stigma, how to talk with people about mental illness, and how to understand her experience as a parent. She found support through her church and NAMI. She accompanies other parents to a support group when their children have escalating symptoms.

Education often relieves fears family members may have about what will happen to their relative as a result of mental illness. Once Sharon realized her young adult daughter, Gabrielle, was not going to be violent or engage in illegal behavior, she "put things into perspective" and "got really educated on bipolar." She looked into research on managing the illness. She observed that reflecting on how Gabrielle experienced their interactions and then revising her responses to her daughter contributes to collaborative decisions about symptom management.

Family members aggressively pursued education on mental illness and treatment, which contributed to their ability to help their relative find needed resources and treatment. This was a key strategy in making their journey through the mental illness maze. Increased understanding of their relative's difficulties led to a compassionate response. One-half of study participants went on to seek service careers involving mental health education or volunteered for NAMI by teaching a Family-to-Family class or leading a support group. They clearly valued mental health education for themselves and the community.

KEY CHAPTER MESSAGES

1. Stigma and discrimination add stress to the lives of both individuals who live with a mental illness and their family members. Stigma occurs when someone is viewed negatively because they have a mental illness. Discrimination occurs when someone is treated in a negative way because they have a mental illness.

2. When family members internalize stigma and carry it with them, the burden of stigma damages their relationships and well-being.

3. Risk factors for developing a mental illness include genetic factors and environmental factors such as stressful life circumstances and a history of trauma.

4. Mental illness affects thoughts, feelings, and behaviors and occurs on a continuum from mild to serious symptoms.

5. Diagnosing a mental illness is a complex process based on observations of behavior and descriptions given by the individual experiencing symptoms. Often, several episodes of symptom patterns occur before a specific diagnosis can be made.

6. Family members need to rely on an assortment of resources to assist them in supporting and caring for their relative. Relying on healthcare and social services prevents emotional and physical exhaustion and increases the ability to find compassion for one's relative.

7. Treatment options include medication, therapy, and support programs. Often, treatment plans integrate medication with other treatment modalities, therapy, and self-management wellness strategies.

Chapter 3

PRACTICE PATIENCE WHEN FACING ADVERSITY

Patience is the tendency to wait calmly
in the face of frustration or adversity
(Sarah Schnitker, 2012).[1]

Getting educated about mental illness takes time. It is impossible to immediately absorb so much new information while also coping with emotions that send us reeling. The confusion of trying to navigate a complex and fragmented mental healthcare system (a huge part of the mental illness maze) adds to the learning curve for finding resources to address your relative's mental health needs.

You may be confronted with frightening behaviors from your relative that do not make sense given their past behavior patterns. You may connect their strange behavior to another event, such as drug use or a head injury. When your relative does not return to normal behavior, confusion escalates about what is happening. Sometimes a mental health crisis leads to hospitalization. It is that first hospitalization that often results in confronting the possibility that your relative is living with a mental illness, thereby starting your journey through the maze.

Your emotional journey as you strive to support your relative also takes time. This chapter highlights how family members first experienced the shock of seeing symptoms of mental illness in a relative. They needed time to understand and to move on to acceptance. As you read about their experiences, think about how the initial shock of seeing mental illness symptoms appear in your relative may have stopped you in your tracks. Later in the chapter, you will learn about predictable emotional responses typically experienced by family members and tips for developing patience as you adjust to changes introduced by mental illness in family life.

PARENT STORIES

For the parents interviewed in my study, the recognition that their adult child lives with a mental illness was fraught with chaos, confusion, shock, anger, and denial. They often looked for other explanations for their child's behavior, such as alcohol or drug use or a physical problem. Times of crisis—such as suicide attempts, incarceration, disappearance, homelessness, or repeated hospitalizations—brought trauma. Parents were bewildered by their adult child's grandiose and delusional thinking, substance abuse, or disastrous financial decisions. Some feared their child would be harmed, and sometimes they were afraid of their child. After a period of denial about the possibility of a mental illness diagnosis, parents

---

talked about feeling guilty, thinking they caused their child's illness. Some felt shame and were fearful of being judged or blamed by others. Their child's unpredictable, upsetting, and disruptive behavior led to feelings of frustration and anger.

Joann Tried to Fix Her Son

Joann's son, Jacob, first showed symptoms of bipolar disorder at age 19. In the midst of a psychotic episode, he awakened his parents at 1 a.m. and claimed someone was coming to the house to kill his brother. When Jacob couldn't be calmed, his family took him to the hospital. Joann put aside most of her responsibilities after Jacob's first hospitalization. As she invested all of her time into caring for her son and her ailing mother, she realized she was not taking care of herself. After desperately trying to control and manage her emotions, Joann concluded she could not fix Jacob's problem and sought support to help her cope.

Anita Asked Why

Anita's daughter, Serena, exhibited symptoms of mental illness after returning home from her first year at college. Early that summer, Anita and her husband discovered Serena had left the house in the middle of the night.

> She wasn't there. We called all her friends. We got in our cars and we split up. We were screaming for her. I drove down to the river, slowly and scanning, and I heard her voice down there. She had run down to

the river in shorts and her bra. She had her phone, a dream catcher, and all these other things. She just threw them as she was running...She was in mania and she thought she could fly. She thought she was a fairy. Some kids found her on a cliff on the river and they talked her away from it. I called my husband, and he came and we took her to the hospital.

Although Serena calmed down with medications, Anita did not initially accept the diagnosis of bipolar disorder, believing that it was a physical problem—possibly related to a concussion in Serena's past.

Anita's younger daughter, Nina, encountered difficulty during her sophomore year of high school. She lacked friends, became sexually provocative, would not talk to her parents, and was eventually hospitalized for escalating symptoms. Anita struggled to figure out what was happening with her daughters. She wondered, "Is it my parenting? Is it that she's a teenager? Is it adoption? Is it identity in a transracial adoption? Is it the change in school? What is going on?"

To process her experiences with her children's mental illness symptoms, Anita visualized her emotions through art. Her artistic expression gave her time to reflect, understand, and move on to accepting that her daughters live with mental illness.

PARTNER/SPOUSE STORIES

As they tried to understand what was happening, partners and spouses struggled with uncertainty and unpredictability brought on by their partner's unexpected and troubling behavior. One partner thought the problem might be related to her partner's midlife crisis. Another wondered if she was to blame, thinking there was something wrong with her. Several thought they did not deserve the situation. They struggled to keep their daily life going through each crisis, "stuffing" their feelings in order to deal with immediate demands. As the disruptive symptoms continued, they experienced chaotic life changes—taking time off work, moving out of their home for safety reasons, getting a restraining order for protection, and not being able to depend on their partner to meet family needs.

Jim Adjusted to Life Changes

About 10 years ago, Jim noticed that his wife, Monica, frequently moved between high and low mood states. She started calling in sick to work on a regular basis. Then, one day, she told him she was feeling suicidal. They went to the hospital together, and Monica was admitted. Jim was forced to adjust to changes in his daily life, including managing childcare for his young son. He spoke about the importance of having patience, letting go of previous life desires, and developing a new pattern for meeting family needs.

Marta Tried to Keep It All Together

Seven years ago, Marta saw behavioral changes in Tim, her partner of 20 years. At first, she wondered if he was going through a midlife crisis. He started to have panic attacks and excessive anxiety, especially when driving or riding in vehicles. He walked incessantly; stopped enjoying things he used to; had problems sleeping; and lost his appetite, resulting in weight loss. Then, Tim abruptly retired from his job in a school system—a position he had held for over 15 years. He made disastrous financial decisions and talked about joining a motorcycle gang. His drinking increased along with making irrational decisions. Although Marta realized Tim had grandiose ideas and was unrealistic about work possibilities, she tried to understand and support him.

> *He's big into music and played occasionally in a band. He was saying he was traveling the world and he was going to be playing at the Excel Center and he's going to fly out to Vegas. Now that I learned more about it, that was kind of a grandeur stage. He was untouchable.*

She hypothesized that Tim's work—teaching kids with major behavior problems—was stressful, and suspected he was drinking after work to manage his stress. He talked about buying an expensive, top-of-the-line motorcycle and opening a restaurant because he loved food. Marta recognized that Tim's behavior did not seem right. She can now see that life during these times was "quite a struggle."

> *I was probably more of an enabler in the beginning because I felt like I was trying to keep it all together, not even really being aware of what it was. Maybe this is just 43; he's thinking maybe life is over. Crisis, panic stage. I was just trying to keep it all together— the kids. Normal type stuff.*

As Tim's symptoms became more problematic, Marta had to quickly close their joint account because money and belongings in their home were disappearing. Eventually, Marta realized she needed to protect her two children and her home and made the decision to separate from Tim.

SIBLING STORIES

Siblings often first hear about their brother or sister's disturbing behaviors from their parents. Their sibling's symptoms—such as hearing voices, irritability, self-isolation, and difficulty getting along with others—can bring unpredictability and sometimes chaos into family relationships. Harmful behaviors like suicide attempts, homelessness, and actions leading to incarceration caused immense worry and concern for the well siblings I interviewed. They experienced an onslaught of emotions: anxiety, fear, confusion, frustration, sadness, uncertainty, and shame. Some study participants were angry at their sibling for making life difficult for their parents. They felt the loss of the brother or sister they used to have. Initially, siblings offered support to their parents—who had the major responsibility of responding to the needs of the ill sibling. However, over time, well siblings took on added responsibility as their parents aged.

Katie Tried to Save Her Family

Katie remembers that her younger brother, Kevin, did not like to listen to authority and became easily frustrated. At age 18, he frequently drank alcohol, drove while drinking, and used illegal drugs. As a freshman in college, Kevin had a psychotic episode. Katie recalled,

He was like a different person. It was really scary be-
cause you could tell he was in a different world…I
think it was a common reaction of feeling scared, like,
where is my brother? Where did he go? Wondering is
he addicted to drugs…Back then I had no idea about
anything. I ended up getting the "I'll save my family"
complex and did that for many, many years, where
I was always the one helping him and trying to help
my mom.

After spending years trying to help her mother make decisions about her brother's mental healthcare, Katie realized the necessity of managing her life stress so she could stay healthy for her own family—her husband and two children.

Janet Tried to Support Her Parents

While in college, Janet found out about her brother's "goofy" behavior when he was 18 or 19. David, four years younger, talked very fast and made a dangerous plan to drive a snowmobile over 30 miles through fenced fields. Janet came home from college to support her mother, but they didn't know what to do. After consulting with a doctor and a priest, David was admitted to a hospital. Janet recalled her feelings at the time:

I was a young adult and I was in shock, probably, be-
cause I never had experienced anyone being in men-
tal institutions. I was there for my parents. I tried to
be supportive. But it felt like an out-of-control ordeal. I
was helpless in some ways. I responded the best I could

44

by listening to my parents and visiting my brother. I was trying to learn about it.

As their mother aged, Janet and her sister supported one another in monitoring their brother's behavior and care needs.

Heather Faced a Difficult Decision

Heather's brother, Brad, showed symptoms consistent with mental illness one year before he was first hospitalized at age 22 for erratic behavior and saying things that did not make sense. He had run-ins with law enforcement and the courts and then experienced a psychotic break and would not accept help. When he ran away from home, his parents called the police. Heather remembers the changes in Brad during his psychotic break. "I couldn't recognize him at all. His eyes were different. I couldn't connect with him. It was like someone totally different had gone into his brain."

Then, Heather's life became more complex when, after dating for over a year, her boyfriend Scott told her he lived with bipolar disorder.

I had no idea. He had to tell me. I didn't guess. I didn't have any clues about it. He's really high functioning. You wouldn't know unless he told you. He said I was the first person he told outside his family.

Heather struggled with reconciling her reactions to her brother's illness in the midst of thinking about what Scott's diagnosis would mean for a life together. She had to manage her anxiety about the decision to marry Scott.

I didn't understand it completely. The most nervous I ever felt. I took a NAMI [National Alliance on Mental Illness] Family-to-Family class. Someone in there was married to someone with bipolar disorder. I was there mostly to talk about my brother, but when she found out [my boyfriend] also had it, she really warned me and said don't get married because she had such a bad experience. I had to really recognize that was her experience and didn't mean that's what I would have.

It took time for Heather to realize a difference existed between how her brother and Scott, now her husband, managed symptoms of bipolar disorder.

ADULT CHILDREN STORIES

When they were children, the adults I interviewed—who are now in their 30s and older—observed problematic and bizarre symptoms in their ill parent. Some experienced trauma that interrupted a stable family life. Several were alone when their parent had a mental health crisis, and they needed to get help. Their initial confusion about what was happening to their parent was followed by a range of emotions, including anger, embarrassment, and guilt. Several took on blame when they thought they caused their parent's illness or wanted to avoid making it worse.

Sam Had a Very Responsible Childhood

In sixth grade, Sam realized his family was different from others.

Mom was in the hospital a lot, but it wasn't to fix a broken leg. It wasn't for cancer treatment. My dad, my sister, and I would go visit Mom on Sundays in the hospital. It was a huge building, and as a little kid I would have never found my way out of it if Dad hadn't known the way. Sometimes Mom was very sad, and sometimes Mom was good-natured.

He realized that other kids did not visit their mothers in a hospital on Sundays. His mother, Miriam, would show him the artwork she had made while hospitalized. He wondered why adults were in the hospital doing art. As he grew older, Sam took responsibility for monitoring his mother's medications.

I don't think I had much opportunity to be innocent as a child because I was often on duty. I would have to dispense the medicine when it wasn't a time that my dad was at home. We'd have to vary where we hid the medicine so she wouldn't find it and then try a suicidal overdose. I remember where it would be hidden different times, and I'd have my little assignment sheet—this was when I was 12 years old—two pink, one blue, one white. Then, I would have to give those at the right time and be really careful that she wasn't spying on me. I'd hide the stash. I was all-consumed, and I was afraid to go very far and have very much fun because I felt like I should be on duty. In fact, Mom would call me her warden in the fun sense. I had a very responsible childhood.

Sam's worst times were during his mother's depressive episodes, when she would sit up all night, smoking cigarette after cigarette, and then sleep all day. For Sam, when "Mom wasn't depressed, then everything's good."

Jessica Benefitted from Therapy

At age 15, Jessica discovered that her mother, Diane, lived with a mental illness when she came home from an after-school job and found her acting strangely. Diane, normally cautious with money, bestowed Jessica with gifts from shopping trips, had dressed-up teddy bears, and had packed school lunches the size of a grocery bag. Bewildered, Jessica called her dad for help. She later learned that her mother was first diagnosed with a mental illness at age 17.

Now, Jessica is grateful to her mother for arranging for her to see a therapist. She noted, "My mom always wanted to make sure that stuff wasn't affecting us. I didn't know what mental illness was. It wasn't something that was talked about." Jessica benefitted from therapy as a teenager and continued to see the same therapist as a young adult.

Mark Grew Up Without a Father Figure

Mark lived most of his early years in the shadow of his father's mental illness. With a lack of family and community support in his later childhood and teenage years, he struggled to make sense of what had happened in his family. When Mark was 10, his father, Gene, abruptly left the family home when he was committed to a state hospital for bipolar disorder. Although his father was physically absent, Mark continued to grapple with the consequences of Gene's mental illness.

As a 10-year-old, Mark knew something was wrong, but he did not understand what was happening. He remembered his mother talking about his father's car accidents and trying to get help because she knew about Gene's family history of mental illness. After his first hospitalization, Gene came home for a brief period, but quickly relapsed and physically and emotionally abused Mark's mother. At that point, he was deemed to be mentally ill and dangerous and did not live in the family home again. Mark's mother, Janet, became the sole parent for Mark and his two younger siblings.

Before Gene's first hospitalization, Mark had some "okay times" with his father, but he mainly remembers that Gene was mad and mean most of the time. As a teenager, Mark grew up without a father figure. He reflected, "It derailed my life, I think, quite a bit. I didn't have anybody." He has worked diligently to emotionally separate himself from his father and determine who he is and how he wants to live his life.

IT TAKES TIME TO GET HELP

Certainly, we want to find help for our ill family member as quickly as we can. However, it often takes time to recognize that a relative's strange behavior may be connected with symptoms of a mental illness. Then, more time is needed for an ill relative to agree to seek help, which may be followed by even more time to get an appointment with a psychiatrist, psychologist, or therapist, unless a crisis results in immediate hospitalization. An additional delay may occur in the process of finding the right diagnosis and effective treatment. The chaotic, challenging, and often lengthy time period of finding help for an ill family member demands patience with the journey through the mental illness maze. The time frame is usually not days or weeks, but more often months, and sometimes years.

You will also need time for your own emotional journey as you accompany your family member through the process of recognizing that they live with a mental illness and helping them find effective treatment. Right away, family members in my study wanted to fix their ill relative's problem. They needed time to understand and recognize their feelings of confusion, disappointment, anger, frustration, and shame, and they required time to learn about available resources.

HOW TO BE PATIENT

First, recognize that your emotional journey is a process. The NAMI Family-to-Family class curriculum identifies three stages of predictable emotional responses that we experience as we recover from the trauma brought to family life by a relative's mental illness symptoms. Compare where you are in your emotional journey to the following "Predictable Emotional Responses." [2]

1. *Crisis* – Family members first encounter signs and symptoms of mental illness in a relative. This stage may include denial and hoping a relative does not live with a mental illness. During this time, family members need support, comfort, empathy for their difficult situation, and help finding resources.

2. *Coping* – Family members experience a flood of emotions (anger, guilt, resentment, grief) as they understand that their relative lives with a mental illness. They learn to cope by

expressing emotions; becoming educated; networking with others; gaining skills in listening, empathy, and problem-solving; and finding support from peers.

3. *Advocacy* – In this stage, family members grow to understand their relative's challenges and experiences and accept that their relative lives with a mental illness. They re-establish balance in their life and begin to advocate for better mental health services and resources for their relative and for others who live with mental illness.

Although you may have moved into the advocacy stage, when your relative has a mental health crisis, you may find yourself reverting to earlier stages of dealing with the crisis and searching for coping strategies. Then again, you may also move through the earlier stages more quickly and return to advocacy sooner.

All the family members in my study experienced the three stages of emotional responses. They spent time in crisis, they learned to cope with conflicting emotions, and many moved on to advocating for improved mental healthcare for their relative and others living with a mental illness. As you strive to support your relative, refer to these stages to better understand your experience.

In addition, be patient with yourself. Your relative's mental illness is not your fault; nor is it their fault. In retrospect, you may find yourself thinking you should have done something differently. Be mindful that you used the best knowledge and understanding you had at the time.

Patience is the ability to wait calmly in the face of frustration and adversity.[1] We need to cultivate patience in interpersonal relationships, life hardships, and daily hassles, all of which impact our lives when we have a family member living with a mental illness.

Research confirms that patience is a good thing, linking this characteristic to life satisfaction, self-esteem, self-control, and goal accomplishment.[2] Patience brings a sense of calmness and helps one to know when to act and when to reserve energy for a later time. We can think of patience as helping us get ready to act. Of course, taking patience to an extreme could result in not acting when action is needed. If a relative's behavior places them or others at risk, quick action is required in responding to a crisis situation.

Patience can be learned. Consider the following three steps to practice patience.[3]

1. *Identify why you are impatient and what you are feeling:* When your life is disrupted by your ill relative's behavior, you will likely feel responsible and/or obligated to make things better. You may see yourself as the "fixer" of family problems, resulting in frustration when your efforts do not solve the problem. You may feel helpless because you do not know what to do.

2. *Reframe how you think about the situation:* Recognize that you do not have control over your relative's behavior. You *do* have control over how you view the situation and can strategize about how to manage stressful life experiences.

3. *Think with your purpose in mind:* Plan to persevere with actions needed to encourage your relative to seek help and treatment. Also, realize that you need to give yourself time to manage your own emotions—you must reserve space for your well-being in the midst of the chaos and disruption in your family environment. Doing so will give you the energy you need to provide support to your relative.

52

Finally, consider the wisdom about patience illustrated in the following quotes.[4]

- *Have patience with all things, but first of all with yourself.*—Saint Francis de Sales
- *Patience is not simply the ability to wait—it's how we behave while we're waiting.*—Joyce Meyer

KEY CHAPTER MESSAGES

1. It takes time to come to terms with the shock of seeing symptoms of mental illness in your relative.

2. Realizing that a relative has a mental illness unleashes a flood of overwhelming emotions (anger, guilt, shame, disappointment, sadness). These are normal responses.

3. A relative's mental illness is no one's fault.

4. Family members need time to understand their emotional responses to having a relative who lives with a mental illness.

5. Typically, family members experience three stages of predictable emotional responses in the process of reaching acceptance that a relative has a mental illness: crisis, coping, and advocacy.

6. Family members benefit from learning to be patient as they experience interpersonal challenges, life hardships, and daily hassles resulting from a relative's symptoms of mental illness.

7. You can develop patience by identifying when you are impatient and what you are feeling, reframing how you think about the situation, and moving forward with your purpose in mind.

Chapter 4

RECALIBRATE EXPECTATIONS

*Setting realistic expectations actually helps
us grow and become more flexible.
It helps us savor life and embrace the messy moments
(Margarita Tartakovsky, 2018).*[1]

Although our expectations motivate us to take action to meet our goals, sometimes they are unrealistic and set us up for disappointment and failure. When a relative lives with a mental illness, unrealistic expectations for their recovery may lead to repeated loss and grief for family members. It is important to acknowledge loss and grief as part of our own recovery, but we don't want to stay trapped in a constant grief mindset that prevents us from making progress in the maze journey.

Treatment for mental illness has a wide range of effectiveness. Sometimes, after a first episode of mental illness, symptoms may not recur. Perhaps a physical problem or stressful event led to the episode. Some individuals living with a mental illness find stability in work and family life by maintaining effective treatment. Others experience repeated episodes of symptoms and hospitalizations, lack insight, and are unable to acknowledge that they live with a mental illness. In recovery, many individuals learn to accept their limitations, manage their illness through medication and therapy, and live a satisfying life within a framework of changed expectations.

Given the variability of outcomes for people living with a mental illness, we can see that it is likely unrealistic to expect a relative to return to the same life they had prior to the emergence of symptoms. Family members in my study needed to change their expectations for their relative's life and become more realistic about what was possible. In this chapter, you will learn about how the family members coped by adjusting their expectations—and what you can do to manage your own expectations.

PARENT STORIES

The parents I interviewed discovered they needed to give up future dreams for their adult children who live with a mental illness.

Connie Realized Her Future Would Be Different

Connie expressed sadness over a changed future for her daughter, Naomi, and the loss of her retirement plans. She lamented, "This is not the future that your child imagined for herself. It's not what you imagined for her. There's that loss of dreams you don't even know you have for your kid." Although Connie and her husband planned to retire to Hawaii, where Connie grew up, they now realize that plan may not be possible. They made financial sacrifices to help Naomi manage her bipolar illness, including paying a huge bill for Naomi's hospitalization following a mental health crisis. Their expectations for family holiday time together changed when, in response to Naomi's scary actions, Connie filed an order of protection to keep her away from the family home. When Naomi became well enough to attend family gatherings but still wasn't allowed at the home, they found a creative solution. Connie's pastor offered them space at the church to use; they celebrated Christmas, birthdays, and other holidays there over a period of two years. It was hard work, but they figured it out.

Joann Grieved the Loss of Dreams for Her Son's Success

Joann remembers her son, Jacob, as a young man with ambition and drive; now he spends a lot of time in bed. Before the onset of his bipolar illness, Jacob had always worked. He kept control of his finances; paid his bills; and bought a car, obtaining a loan on his own without a cosigner. He successfully started a small business, arranged for contracting, and paid the taxes. Joann applauded his responsible behavior, observing, "I don't know a lot of young adults who would be that responsible at that age." After Jacob had several hospitalizations, Joann expressed anguish over the loss of what she hoped her son would be.

> *You have all these dreams for your children. Everything that you think they are so capable of doing is ripped out from underneath you. You grieve the child that you knew. And you're not*

sure if that child is ever going to come back. That's a huge piece of grief that I carry, because I don't have that hope that I'm seeing my baby in there somewhere right now. I have that feeling of loss— like I'm never going to get that child back, or all of my hopes that I had for him and all the stuff that he used to talk about before, and what he wanted to achieve in life.

Joann acknowledged that she is still working on letting go of past dreams for Jacob. She now celebrates the small steps in her son's improvement and fiercely advocates to help him find the treatment and resources needed for his recovery.

Anita Understood Her Daughters' Futures Would Be Different

As a teacher, Anita often attended her students' graduation parties. She spoke about the difficulty of attending the graduations of others while facing the loss of the celebration of her daughter Serena's graduation.

Every kid I taught, if they invited me to their party, I would go there and give them a card and some money. Now, I just feel it's so hard. It's almost like going to someone's baby shower when they're pregnant and I'm infertile. It's the same thing— feels like that dream, that loss. My daughter's class would be graduating this year from college. I'm sure I'm going to experience that loss. It's going to be hard.

Since her younger daughter, Nina, also lives with a mental illness, Anita is facing the reality that her two young adult daughters may continue to be dependent in the future.

> *I remember holding each of my girls when they were tiny babies and wanting to see who they would be in 25 years. I expected Serena to go to college. But now that she is working at a doggie day care, I can see that she is happy with that. [When my daughters were babies], I really thought it would be all nurture. I just thought, we're going to take this girl and we're going to give her everything. She's going to be better than us and able to function higher and able to do so much better.*

Now Anita realizes that Serena has found a fulfilling job. She accepts that Serena's life choices are different from those she had envisioned for her. Anita reflected, "We're still helping them to support their dreams, in a way. But it looks different. It's a different picture."

PARTNER/SPOUSE STORIES

Of the five partners and spouses interviewed for my study, three stayed in relationships with their ill partner. All three experienced chaos and disruption in family life brought on by their partner's symptoms. However, they adapted by changing their expectations for their partner's contributions, taking on the role of caregiver, supporting their partner through challenging times, and encouraging treatment that led to greater stability. The two partners who left their relationships did so to protect their children from the trauma resulting from their ill partner's severe symptoms.

Brenda Managed Her Expectations One Day at a Time

Brenda married her husband, Don, knowing that he lived with bipolar disorder. At the time, he had a stable life and had worked for a food company for 17 years. He also completed a two-year accounting degree, graduating with honors. When they married, Brenda moved in with Don and his mother. Don became depressed after his mother moved to long-term care because she had dementia. Then, Don's manic behavior led to jail time, hospitalizations, and great financial loss. Brenda moved out of the family home for a short time because she feared for her safety.

Now back together with Don, Brenda works full time and has moved into a caretaker role in their relationship. They established a routine that works for them. Brenda gardens and keeps up with exercise. Don is more active in the summer but hibernates in the winter, sleeping until late in the morning. He drives to town to get the paper and reads but does not have other hobbies.

The couple has adjusted to the loss of intimacy caused by the effects of Don's medications. Don told Brenda, "We can cuddle, we can hug and kiss, but that's as far as it goes." Brenda says she can deal with that because "It's not the running force in our life." She is pleased that Don is now more open to discussing finances and his feelings than in the past. He doesn't remember most of his bizarre behavior, which is not uncommon during extreme mood swings. Brenda has let go of the past, reflecting, "That's done and over with. We make the best of today and we go forward." She is working on balancing trust and limit setting in her relationship with Don and has come to understand his challenges arising from his symptoms.

> *I wake up at five-thirty, six o'clock in the morning and I just can't wait to get out in the garden. It makes me really sit back and look at how miserable Don must be, or how anxious. He's told me there's times when he will stay in bed until one, two o'clock in the afternoon because he's afraid something will break or something will go wrong.*

Don continues to complain about memory problems and anxiety. He told Brenda, "This is as good as it's going to get," and does not want to make any more medication changes. Brenda is saving money for retirement in eight years but realizes their situation could change. She manages her expectations by dealing with one day at a time. She observed, "That's all you can do to make the best of each day. Because I learned too well how things can change in an instant." She sees relationships and families as most important and has learned to let go of "stuff" and simplify life.

Jim Learned to Appreciate a Simpler Life

Jim made drastic financial changes to his lifestyle after his wife, Monica, could no longer handle work responsibilities as a teacher because of her symptoms. Given their money situation, he stopped going on the twice-annual fishing trips he used to take. The couple battled back from home foreclosure three times after Monica stopped working. Although Monica receives Social Security disability benefits, she and Jim can no longer sustain their previous lifestyle. Jim sees his friends doing things that he and Monica cannot afford, like going on vacation. He talked about his changed reality.

> *There's a couple of times I felt down about myself a little bit. You see how everybody else is living. You used to live like that. Well, what the hell. You come back to reality and you get to that point where you just say, this is what it is. Do the best you can with it.*

When contemplating the future, Jim realizes he and Monica will not have the bigger house, travel opportunities, and newer cars he once thought they would have later in life. At the same time, however, he discovered that he and Monica now have a better understanding of one another's needs, and they have learned to appreciate a simpler lifestyle.

> *She knows I need to get away with the guys every now and then. I know she needs to go and do her thing, her church, which is very important to her. I know she needs that. You discover you don't really need the money to be happy…It used to be if you want to be happy, go buy something. Let's do this. Let's go do that. You find other things to enjoy. Whether it's watching a TV show or just simple things like taking a walk. You really alter your lifestyle to keep it more simplistic where it's not so dependent on getting all these nice things to make yourself feel better.*

Jim manages his expectations by accepting his role as a caregiver and choosing to enjoy a simpler lifestyle. Monica and Jim view meaningful relationships as most important. They understand

62

the challenges they each face and adjust their actions to promote a peaceful relationship while maintaining realistic expectations for themselves.

SIBLING STORIES

The siblings I interviewed learned to adjust their responses to their ill sibling as they moderated their expectations. Their expectations changed after they learned more about mental illness, observed patterns of behavior in their sibling, and engaged in self-reflection.

Katie Said No to Spending Holidays Together

Katie confided that the situation with her younger brother, Kevin, sometimes feels hopeless. Kevin first exhibited symptoms of a mental illness at age 19 and was later diagnosed with schizoaffective bipolar disorder. She believes he is getting worse with age and has become more realistic about the difficulty of helping her brother. She observed, "I kept really wanting to help him, and thinking for many years that I could, and then realizing he's got a really tough diagnosis." Katie described how, given Kevin's unpredictability, she needed to become more realistic about the challenge of spending holidays together with her extended family.

> *There have been times when we all have left during the middle of family gatherings because of his mood swings...In the past, my mom would try to convince us all that everything was okay. [She*

would say], "Okay Kevin, it's all good now. Let's all have a nice meal together." For many years we acted like it was okay. Then things changed. We said, "No, this isn't okay. He needs help and there's got to be consequences for some of his actions. We're not going to stay in a situation where we're disrespected or feel unsafe."

Katie talked about how her life has been affected by Kevin's illness and other challenges with her siblings. She believed she had to be "the perfect kid."

I didn't want to be the problem child, so I followed the rules. I felt my job was to support my mom, be there for her, and be a mother to her, be a mother to my brother. Be the strong one. We can rely on Katie. She'll know what to do. Talking to the police. It made me very depressed. It made me very anxious. It made me very sad, stressed, and angry.

Through therapy, Katie realized all her efforts were not helping Kevin and her mother. She changed her focus to finding well-being for herself, her husband, and her two children rather than fixating on trying to help her brother.

Heather Accepted Her Brother's Limitations

Heather changed her expectations of her brother, Brad, to fit with the limitations imposed by his symptoms. She spoke about her brother with pride when sharing his accomplishments while living with bipolar disorder. He went back to school and finished college with support from Heather's father. Brad set a goal and worked toward it with determination. Heather reflected, "He's teaching me about how to be determined and independent. I'm lucky to have him. He has so much to offer the world if you just find the right place for him."

In the past, Heather tried to help Brad prepare for a job search by coaching him on writing a resume and improving his personal hygiene, but he resisted her attempts to help.

> *I had to recognize I was being too pushy and it's not my place to give him these things…I decided instead of trying to change my brother I would channel all of that energy into advocacy. That's been a much better outlet for everybody.*

In communicating with her brother, Heather has learned how to be on his side. When Brad had delusions about planes or the president, Heather first tried to be logical and tell him it wasn't true. She realized that approach would elicit a negative response from Brad, and they would end up fighting.

> *Because to him it's real. It's like I'm calling him a liar. I don't want that. That breaks trust, and I'm trying to build trust. I'm on the same side, and I say, 'I'm not sure I agree, but okay, tell me more.' Or you just accept it and move on.*

Heather developed a meaningful relationship with her brother because she changed her expectations of his behavior and what she could do to support him.

ADULT CHILDREN STORIES

Jessica Adjusted Her Expectations of What Was Possible

Jessica found that her mother's symptoms and management of bipolar disorder led to a role reversal in their relationship during her teenage years. She explained, "It's hard when it's your mom. Because when you're a teenager and it's your mom, she's supposed to take care of me. I'm not supposed to be figuring her out." Jessica had to change her expectations to accommodate her mother's need to manage symptoms.

> *When you're a young person and your mom can't go out past 8:30, that's frustrating...What the heck. But my dad was pretty good about taking us out or doing things, or I would find rides. Once I drove, it wasn't an issue.*

Her mother, Diane, is doing well on her medication plan and is involved in Jessica's family life. Their relationship works well because Jessica has adjusted her expectations of what is possible for her mother. There were times when she wanted her mother to come over to help with her children when her husband was away; however, Diane couldn't come over after taking her medication in the evening. Jessica was frustrated until she realized the medication made her mother too drowsy to feel safe outside of her home. Jessica's children were also sometimes disappointed when they were having fun with their grandmother and wanted her to spend the night, but she couldn't because she did not have her medication. Diane now keeps some at Jessica's house for those occasions.

Abby Decided Not to Visit Her Mom in the Hospital

During Abby's childhood, her mother, Mandy, regulated mood changes with medications and support from Abby's father. Recently, Mandy's psychiatric medication became less effective following treatment for breast cancer. She developed manic symptoms, believed the devil was chasing her, and went missing for a short period of time after a car accident. Three hospitalizations followed owing to difficulty in finding effective treatment. During this time, Abby juggled a new job, parenting, and a move to a new house. Also, her father faced surgery for a cancer diagnosis. Given the many competing demands for her time and attention, Abby decided she would not visit her mother during the third hospitalization.

> *I just can't. It's really stressful to visit her. It's stressful to talk on the phone with her. I try and call her, but I don't know if I can take on this emotional [burden]. There's the guilt that goes along with that, of course. It's not an easy decision.*

Abby's aunt (Mandy's sister) criticized the family's response to Mandy's crisis. While at home between hospitalizations, Mandy called people saying she was scared and was going to be killed. Abby's aunt decided to help, but her actions were not helpful for the family. During one of Mandy's hospitalizations, the aunt sent a text to Abby and her brother admonishing them to visit their mom. They did not respond to the text, a choice supported by their father.

We just didn't respond. I had a really big work project for my new job. It was Monday, my dad's surgery, and my first big work project. Thursday was my next work project presentation and she ended up texting me also on Thursday—a group text to 10 people saying, "Abby, when was the last time you visited your mom?" My dad ended up talking to her. This is not what my family needs right now.

Abby did not know how to deal with her aunt and was grateful for her father's advocacy. She explained that she and her brother have a right to choose their level of involvement and do not need to feel additional guilt in response to their aunt's actions. Abby realizes she has lost the mother she would like to have.

I think when all this [the car accident] first happened, my mom was not her. That's not my mom anymore. I think that was hard. She hasn't been able to transition with us well into adulthood. I felt, even in college, the loss of my mother. When I would call her, she would want to talk about something that made her mad or say, "Oh, I don't like calling you anymore." I felt kind of lost and then disconnected…You don't feel like mom anymore. But you're my mom by title. You're supposed to be here. You're not supposed to be the one causing this.

Although Mandy does not provide the typical mother role for her children, Abby has learned to "take a step back" and consider what is possible for her mother. She would like to see her "get to a place where she is comfortable with herself" and identify her feelings. At this point, Mandy's future is uncertain, and she told Abby that she wonders if she will always have scary thoughts and be sad. During her mother's hospitalizations, Abby and family members rotated the responsibility of visiting Mandy. However, Abby now sees the stress that resulted for them.

> *Looking back on it, my mother didn't even know what was going on then. Not that we shouldn't have visited her, but we strained ourselves and our work life. We strained our relationships with our significant others slightly because "I need to go visit my mom." You're doing all these things. I just don't think that one person can change chemical imbalance. That's what we all thought—if we make her happy, she'll get out of this.*

Abby moderated her expectations for what she could do to help her mother. Now, she would love to see her mom handle an independent life; her hopes and dreams for her mother have changed.

LETTING GO OF UNREALISTIC EXPECTATIONS

Family members in my study revised their expectations when they realized the demands and limitations imposed by a mental illness made their previous expectations for their relative's behavior and accomplishments unrealistic. They began to celebrate small changes and efforts their relative made toward recovery while managing symptoms and treatment, and they expressed appreciation for their relative's accomplishments in the face of mental illness symptoms. They worked to separate symptoms from the essence and uniqueness of their relative. In addition, they learned to moderate their own expectations for what they could do for their relative. They realized that having unrealistic expectations for themselves would contribute to negative emotions (guilt, anger, disappointment, frustration). By letting go of unrealistic expectations, family members engaged in behaviors that supported their relative's well-being.

HOW WE CREATE EXPECTATIONS

Expectations are beliefs about the future and the likelihood of an event happening. We combine our past knowledge and experiences to create expectations for the future, which then drive our behavior.[2] For example, previous success in accomplishing a goal (high school graduation) contributes to our belief in the likelihood of future success and motivates our behavior to work toward the next goal (college graduation). In this case, our expectations will likely be beneficial, since having expectations for success is a positive motivator for action.

Expectations give us a road map for our behavior and increase our confidence as we travel with a relative through the mental illness maze. Typically, we are optimistic about our expectations, since we like to imagine a positive future. However, expectations may be disconfirmed when the anticipated event or situation does not occur.

To understand a discrepancy between expectations and outcome, we can work on developing greater awareness and vigilance about what is happening. We can engage in problem-solving and modify our behavior, or we can change inaccurate beliefs. We try to make sense of discrepancies between our expectations and reality by: 1) ignoring the discrepancy, 2) keeping the discrepancy in mind for a future action, 3) mindfully connecting the discrepancy between our expectation and the event that does not match our expectations, and 4) revising our understanding of what has happened.[2] We can act to address the difference between our expectations and reality. When the expected outcome does not happen, regret and disappointment are motivators for changing our behavior. If we continue to take the same actions based on unchanged expectations, the likely result is continued disappointment or failure.

> *If you always do what you've always done, you'll always get what you've always got* (attributed to various authors).

Think about these examples of unrealistic expectations that are likely to lead to stress and disappointment:[1]

- Everyone should like me.
- The world should be fair.
- My golden years were supposed to golden.

We do not have control over these outcomes, nor do we have control over the behaviors and choices of our family members. However, we can learn to make our expectations more realistic. In a new situation, mindfully examine your expectations by taking these actions: 1) ask yourself what you expect, 2) determine the source or reason for your expectation, and 3) ask yourself if your expectation is realistic. When your expectation leads to a disappointing outcome and you determine the expectation was unrealistic, plan what you need to do differently and adjust your expectation to match reality.[3]

71

HOW TO MANAGE EXPECTATIONS

Consider the following practical suggestions for revising unrealistic expectations.[1]

- Keep a list of unrealistic expectations and realize that you will make mistakes in matching expectations to reality.
- Imagine how you would talk to someone else with the same unrealistic expectation. This will make your self-talk more reasonable and compassionate.
- Evaluate whether your expectation helped you move toward what you wanted to occur. If it didn't, acknowledge that it may be prudent to revise your expectation.
- Be compassionate with yourself and others. This will help you develop healthy beliefs and focus on what is possible.
- Be flexible in adapting to changing circumstances.
- Create new beliefs that help you achieve a realistic expectation.

We especially need to pay attention to the belief that we are "not enough."[4] This is a false belief that we should discard and replace with our own story of value and self-worth. We will never be perfect. Perfection is definitely an unrealistic expectation. While we may want to set high expectations for ourselves, we may need to revise them to be realistic. Crafting realistic expectations will make your journey through the mental illness maze possible.

To stop expecting too much of yourself, realize that you are not perfect and making mistakes is part of the learning process. Avoid comparing yourself to others. Some days are good, some are not as good; recognize there are days you may not be able to do your best. Find the positives in life, be kind to yourself, and learn to love who you are.[5] When you let go of unrealistic expectations, you will be free to find reasonable and effective strategies for contributing to your relative's well-being. Healthy, realistic expectations will make it possible to support your relative without resentment and anger and will contribute to greater calm and wellness in your life.

KEY CHAPTER MESSAGES

1. Expectations are beliefs about the future and the likelihood that an event will happen or a goal will be reached.

2. Expectations can motivate us to take action to meet a goal.

3. Unrealistic expectations contribute to frustration, disappointment, and stress.

4. When a relative experiences symptoms of mental illness, we often need to revise our expectations for their role in the family or what they will accomplish.

5. Examining and revising our expectations will help us develop more realistic expectations.

6. Replace the belief that you are "not enough" with your own story of value and self-worth.

7. Recognize and accept that you are not perfect and that is okay.

8. It is not realistic to expect to control our family members' behavior.

9. Revising unrealistic expectations will lead to greater well-being for your relative living with a mental illness and for yourself.

Chapter 5

REFRAME RELATIONSHIPS TO MANAGE STRESS

*Reframing is a way of changing the way you look
at something and, thus, changing your experience of it.
It can turn a stressful event into either major trauma
or a challenge to be bravely overcome
(Elizabeth Scott, 2020).[1]*

Bad things do happen to good people. No one gets through life without adversity. Mental illness in family life contributes to adversity when difficult relationships result in chaos and disruption. How we view those relationships can impact how we deal with stress in challenging times. While being realistic about our expectations, we can learn to think more positively about our family relationships by reframing the situation.

How did the family members I interviewed reframe their relationship to reduce the stress encountered in their attempts to help their relative? Were they able to find a "silver lining" as they examined the meaning of the relationship? This chapter describes how family members reframed their relationship with their relative and explains how cognitive reframing helps us think differently about a situation.

PARENT STORIES

Connie Focused on Honesty

Connie experienced adversity when her young adult daughter, Naomi, exhibited bizarre and scary behavior during manic episodes.

> *I come downstairs and the basement is lit up like a Christmas tree, and she's up. She has taken every family picture and frame and albums and stabbed out her sister's eyes and has ripped photos in half, ripping out her sister's face. She has pulled out all of our tax records, our wills, everything. Papers are everywhere. This is really early in the morning, 4 a.m. I said, "Naomi, you need to stop." She started throwing things at me. She threw a wooden box at me. She tried to set our house on fire. She built a pyre out of the pictures and family albums and paper.*

Connie called the police. At the hospital, Naomi was placed on a 72-hour hold and given a civil commitment for the third time.

When Naomi did not agree to the commitment, Connie testified at mental health court.

As Naomi agreed to take medication and began the recovery process, Connie reframed her relationship with her daughter to one of coaching her on life decisions while respecting her status as a young adult. She has become better at sensitively sharing her observations with Naomi. When Naomi acts fidgety or agitated, Connie asks her if she needs a ride to pick up her medication. Although Connie continues to find some of Naomi's behaviors challenging, she is honest with her daughter about behavior that may mean symptoms are increasing. For example, when having conversations about body odor, Connie learned to be more direct.

> *"Naomi, I need to point out to you that your body odor is really bad and that concerns me for a couple of reasons. One, that means you are not in tune to it; it means you're tuning into something else...Every other time your body odor has gotten out of control is when you're heading into a mania or you're in mania. I need you to know that. When was the last time you ate? When was the last time you slept?" Naomi said, "You know, Mom, that's really mean." I said, "No, it's not mean, because part of your illness is you don't see when you're getting worse. I'm going to point those things out to you because one of your goals is not to be hospitalized. If you want to stay out of the hospital, then we have to look at the signs, and when you don't see the signs, I have asked your other family members to point things out to you, because part of the illness is the lack of insight."*

Although these are difficult conversations to have, especially because Naomi is an adult, Connie has reframed her relationship with Naomi by establishing a new norm for providing direct feedback about troublesome behavior.

Elaine Acknowledged Relationship Challenges

Elaine's daughter, Terry, has threatened suicide in the past and takes medication for bipolar disorder. When describing Terry's life challenges, Elaine reflected on past relationship difficulties with her mother as she considered the relationship with her own daughter. While growing up, Elaine's mother never told her she was loved and asked her to move out of the family home when she became pregnant with Terry at age 17. Currently, Terry has difficulty managing money and developing a stable romantic relationship but lives independently and maintains stability at her job. Elaine wonders how much she should help her daughter with life decisions and desires a more positive mother-daughter relationship. Although she wishes for greater closeness with Terry, she is learning to accept that "this is how it is" and realizes that she can be happy with the relationship they do have. She is coming to terms with what's possible for their relationship.

Elaine tries to follow Terry's cues about needing space, but she is also willing to press Terry on "things that are important." One time, when they were out walking together, Terry became angry about something and went back to the house. Elaine did not try to stop her and talked to her later. She said to Terry, "That was a difficult thing for me to let you go and then to walk and enjoy and not replay the story in my head." They agreed that sometimes communication about their interactions is important for their relationship. While acknowledging the challenges they face, Elaine noted, "Actually, I think it's pretty good for where both of us are at." She reframed her thinking by recognizing she can be satisfied with their relationship, given the challenges they have both experienced in life.

PARTNER/SPOUSE STORIES

Frank Focused on the Good Parts

Frank, now in his 70s, shared past stories about his wife, Gloria, and her actions during manic episodes. Although the couple experienced adversity during their early years together, including alcoholism and Gloria's numerous health problems, he has reframed their relationship to fondly view their last years together. Gloria died five years ago from pancreatic cancer.

> *The last five or 10 years before she died, we got along very well. She was a very pleasant lady...I will always miss her, because at the tail end, she was a very good woman. As we looked back at our life, every once in a while, we would sit down, "Remember when you done that?" No, she couldn't remember.*

Frank's words of advice for others who have family members living with a mental illness show how he understood what would be helpful to Gloria in their relationship.

> *Be firm. Be very kind. Don't let them to get to you, because they really don't mean to do this. Because their*

mind is not working right. If their mind was work-
ing right, they wouldn't be bipolar. Right? Treat them
like a human being. Treat them like you want to be
treated…If she's not manic, thank God for that. If she's
manic, do the best you can at that time. And then let
her go. Don't tie her up and say you can't do this no
more. Let her [have her] freedom. She'd walk outside
and she'd look at the peach trees and blossoms. She'd
go in my garden. If she pulled out something, so what?
Not a big deal.

Frank looks back on his life and accepts that good came out of the couple's life struggles as both learned to deal with adversity. Before Gloria died, she accepted that she was at the end of her life. Frank has no regrets. He reflected, "Every morning when I wake up, [the first thing I do is] thank God that I'm alive. I'm well and I'm as good as I can be."

Marta Focused on Her Children

For Marta, reframing her relationship with her partner, Tim, meant discontinuing that relationship. They separated after 20 years together; she realized the relationship was not safe for her and their two children. One evening, Marta and her son, then age 10, came home from the library. She recalled the traumatic experience.

When I opened the door, I noticed the kitchen win-
dow—the blinds were kind of blowing. There was al-
ready a restraining order in effect at the time. [The
blowing blinds] seemed kind of weird. I thought the

window must have been broken. I thought somebody broke into the house, not thinking [Tim] would have been the one. I went out to call 911...

Tim was in the house and attacked Marta in the presence of their son as she called the police. She discovered that Tim had destroyed "a lot of stuff" in their home. Following the incident, he was arrested and hospitalized until he stabilized on medication; he then went to jail for several months. Marta continues to monitor the contact Tim has with her son and older daughter, now in college, and sought therapy for her son, who witnessed more of Tim's bizarre behaviors than her daughter. She has reframed her situation to find a silver lining in the adversity her family experienced.

It's kind of changed me. I'm more up front and focused and speak my mind and have to do things that I normally wouldn't have done before, because I have to be put in that position now as a single parent. As far as the kids or at work, I've had to make it happen.

Reframing sometimes means leaving a relationship when it becomes too harmful to sustain.

SIBLING STORIES

For the siblings in my study, reframing their relationship with their brother or sister often meant taking on more responsibility when their parents could no longer provide support. Siblings dedicated significant time and energy to "being there" for their ill brother or sister. However, over time they learned they needed to give attention to their own lives and their partners and children. Although they were initially overwhelmed, their sibling's struggles did not dominate their lives. They acknowledged the challenge of taking on responsibility for their brother or sister; they also found meaning and value in caregiving and in increasing their knowledge about mental illness.

Katie Let Go of Her Need to Control

Katie moved from criticizing her brother Kevin's health habits to accepting what helps him cope.

> *What would make Kevin happy? One year for Christmas I gave him a big pack of cigarettes and Mountain Dew. He was beyond thrilled. I've realized through my own research that cigarettes actually calm people who have schizoaffective bipolar and schizophrenia. Smoking obviously isn't healthy, but knowing it provides some sense of calmness for Kevin justifies it in my mind.*

Katie realized she needed to reframe her relationship with Kevin in order to reduce the adversity in her life. Although her concern for Kevin is always present, it is no longer the center of her life. She has learned to detach and finds that "life is better as a result." She reframed her sense of responsibility for managing challenges brought on by Kevin's symptoms of mental illness.

> *I can pray for him. I can be there to talk to him. I can be there when things get rough. That's really all I can*

*do. I can't control what happens to him. I can't talk
him into being different.*

Katie reframed her relationship with her younger brother by letting go of trying to control his behavior.

Carmen Emphasized Her Sister's Strengths

Carmen, who has a husband and children, balances her own
family life with being available for her older sister, Lily. Most of
the time, Lily has a stable life, but she sometimes needs support
from her sister in managing bipolar disorder. Carmen coaches
Lily with helpful suggestions while supporting her independence
and praising her accomplishments. She takes time to promote
Lily's wellness.

> *I hate to see her sad and unhappy, and [supporting
> her] requires more time on my part and more con-
> scious communication with her. Have you talked
> to your sister in a couple of days? You definitely
> need to check in. Or, if I haven't heard from her, I
> don't automatically wonder if something's wrong.
> She and I communicate very well. She says, "Well,
> I'm not having a good day. I have to change my
> medication." We talk through it...It requires more
> time and more energy.*

Since she works from home and has a supportive boss, Carmen
is available for Lily if her symptoms become problematic. She moves
into high gear when Lily experiences a crisis.

I remember very clearly the second suicide attempt. I came home and my husband told me, and I pretty much crumpled to the ground and cried. She's my only sister. The prospect of losing her is extremely emotional and very hurtful. I go through being mad, being very mad, and angry, and sad—all the things I should be going through. I feel all of them. I roll up my sleeves and try to help. "Now we've got to get busy. Get you well and get you on the right path." I get in the car and go to her for one, first and foremost, so I'm with her. I stay with her. I let her go through what's she going through.

Lily currently works as a substitute teacher, usually one day a week; she helps other residents in her apartment complex solve computer problems; and she tutors Carmen's youngest son in math. Carmen admires Lily's accomplishments, saying, "I'm proud of her—the way she contributes and makes a difference. I'm proud of her for giving. She's really an incredible, incredible person." Carmen shared a story about Lily, highlighting how her sister is an effective self-advocate. Lily often takes her cat, Felipe, down to the apartment complex lobby area.

Older ladies that had lost a pet would spend time petting Felipe. She called it pet therapy. Somebody complained. It happened to be a guy who was mad because he wasn't allowed at their Christmas party because he didn't bring anything, so the manager had to tell her Felipe is not allowed in the lobby anymore. Instead of coming to me, she wrote a letter, and it went right to the regional manager. Well, Felipe is now allowed in the lobby. But I didn't find out about this until after. She managed it. I got a text—"Felipe's in the lobby again."

Carmen acknowledges the difficult times in their relationship, but reframes the relationship by emphasizing Lily's strengths and positive contributions to community and family life.

ADULT CHILDREN STORIES

Adult children reframed their childhood family relationships through considerable reflection about what it was like to grow up with a parent who lived with a mental illness. In adulthood, this reflective work led them to reframe past difficult family relationships to recognize that they had become stronger in managing their own life challenges.

Mark Said No to Continued Connection

Mark, whose father, Gene, was institutionalized for mental illness during Mark's childhood, recalls his teenage years as "horrible and rough." He remembers having a lot of anger toward his father and yelling at him on the phone in order to feel okay again. As a young adult, with the help of therapy, Mark reframed his relationship with Gene by saying no to continued interaction with him. He is adamant about moving beyond the shadow of his father's illness.

Nothing positive comes from him anymore. It's more of a burden. The way that impacts me is I obviously don't want to be like him. I just want to shut the door and live my life. I know his illness has changed things in my life. I don't want to be like him. I don't want it to affect me in the future. I don't want it to be part of my life. I want to start new, fresh. "Don't look in the rearview mirror" kind of thing. My day-to-day hope is that I don't become him. I don't go down his path or even close to anything that he's done. I want a future without him.

By reframing his relationship with his father as one that he no longer needs to continue, Mark now focuses on the joy and hope for the future in his current family relationships with his wife and daughter.

Melanie Found Compassion

Melanie explained that she survived childhood "by being quiet and good" when family members were not available for her owing to her father's symptoms of bipolar disorder and her brother Paul's troublesome behaviors. After college, Melanie moved out of the family home to share an apartment with a girlfriend. She was glad to leave, because family life was chaotic with Paul still living at home. She believes some of her life decisions, such as her first marriage that ended in divorce, are connected to dysfunction in her family of origin.

I couldn't be the person that I wanted to be in that household. There was stuff going on that was dysfunctional. My parents weren't able to get help for their son, who was a big contributor to the chaos. Then my dad's illness—that was chaos too. My mother was rather a secretive person—"Don't tell anybody that this is happening." That was the way things were then because nobody knew about mental illness...It was looked on as worse than physical illness.

As an adult, Melanie is working on understanding the dynamics of her past family relationships. She is trying to understand her mother from a more compassionate viewpoint, acknowledging it "was not easy to be in her shoes." Later in life, her mother started taking an antianxiety medication.

My mother wasn't a warm, fuzzy person, so I guess I survived her lack of warmth. When I saw my dad go down, it was like, oh, he's my one solid person I count on...I'm not going to get this person back.

Today, Melanie views her decision to step into the background as a child, given demands on the family stemming from Paul's symptoms, as something that helped her parents and benefited her own approach to life.

This is kind of a sacrifice. I was proud that I was able to do that because that took a lot for a kid. [My parents] had too much on their plate already. This has really helped me thinking that even though I was this kind of withdrawn kid, there were lots of reasons for that...I tried to do my best in high school and college. I got average grades in college. I think I could have done much better. I think I had some mental health issues. I didn't seek any help. I stuck to it and I became a teacher. I love substitute teaching right now. It let me see that I had to postpone gratification, basically. That's what I learned. Stay the course.

Melanie reframed how she viewed difficult family relationships during her childhood. She sees that her choice helped her parents, and that living through challenging times led her to make beneficial life choices for herself.

ENDING AND CREATING DISTANCE IN FAMILY RELATIONSHIPS

These stories provide insight about how reframing relationships helps manage the stress of adversity brought about by a relative's mental illness symptoms. Sometimes, reframing means saying no to continued interactions. It is acceptable and beneficial to withdraw from a relationship that severely compromises one's life choices and well-being. Certainly, this is an extremely difficult and often guilt-producing decision. Two partners and one adult child in my study opted to discontinue relationships, given potential harm to themselves and other family members.

Parents set limits in their relationship with an adult child in order to avoid the consequences of potentially harmful behaviors. One parent had to file an order of protection, several had to call the police, and several opted to support civil commitment for their child. They all continued relationships with their adult child while working to find balance in meeting their own life needs. Some siblings reframed their relationship by distancing themselves from the perceived obligation that they needed to help, while others focused on recognizing their sibling's strengths in living with the limiting effects of a mental illness.

FINDING THE SILVER LINING

How do we find the good in bad times? How do we turn negatives into positives? Most family members found a silver lining in the relationship challenges they encountered in supporting a relative living with a mental illness. A silver lining represents hope in the midst of tough times; finding a silver lining helps us to make sense of bad things that happen.

Family members in the study identified two "silver lining" benefits. First, they focused on their relative's strengths and what they had accomplished while living with challenging limitations. Second, family members now realized good things had occurred from their ongoing quest to support their relative. These positives included finding a whole new community of others who had similar situations—they were no longer alone in their quest. They talked about how much they learned about mental illness, how they had become less judgmental of others, and how they found their voice in advocating for their relative and others who live with a mental illness. They pointed out the self-growth that resulted from managing the stress of adverse situations. Finding a silver lining eased their journey through the mental illness maze.

COGNITIVE REFRAMING

Cognitive reframing helps us see the positive side of family relationships by viewing a situation in a new way. Focusing on positive aspects reduces the stress of being mired in gloom and doom.

In therapy, cognitive reframing helps an individual comprehend the possibility of taking action to improve their situation by altering perceptions about themselves, another, or a situation. Ways to change negative self-perceptions include: 1) having a sense of personal control (within what it is realistic to control); 2) altering perceptions or beliefs that are negative, not true, or self-defeating; 3) converting a negative idea into a positive idea; and 4) using reframing to change behavior and improve well-being.[2]

Our thoughts influence our communication with others. Positive thoughts lead to positive communication in our relationships. Cognitive reframing leads to developing a clearer view of a situation, finding greater insight about what is happening, and questioning inaccurate perceptions.[3] Also, cognitive reframing reduces our stress level—since our bodies respond to our perceptions of stress, perceiving events in a negative light increases our stress response.[3]

How is it possible to change our thinking to be more positive? This sounds like it is easier said than done. Elizabeth Scott, a wellness coach, offers four reframing strategies:[1]

1. Learn about thinking patterns.

2. Notice your thoughts.

3. Challenge your thoughts.

4. Replace your thoughts with more positive thoughts.

You can see there is work to be done before you can simply replace negative thoughts with positive thoughts.

Learn About Thinking Patterns

Negative thinking patterns increase stress. We may hold cognitive distortions, which are skewed beliefs about a relationship, event, or experience. These can involve "all-or-nothing thinking," leading to the assumption that everything is bad. We might overgeneralize, saying that since a bad thing has happened, other situations will be bad. We ignore the positive when we hold onto the negative, or we jump to conclusions. For example, we may get into the negative thinking pattern of predicting the future based on a current experience.[4] Another negative thought pattern involves the way we explain our life experiences. Negative explanatory styles include thinking our difficult situation is permanent, our entire life is affected, and the situation is our fault or another's fault.[5] These negative explanatory styles create stress and become a barrier to coping positively with a situation.

Notice Your Thoughts

Try to observe your thoughts. What are you thinking? Is your thinking negative? You can keep track of your thoughts by writing them down and then examining them to determine whether you have a negative pattern of thinking. Mindfulness or meditation can help you notice your thoughts.

Challenge Your Thoughts

Ask yourself whether negative thoughts are true. Are you engaging in negative self-talk? What are other ways you can view your situation and your relationship with your relative? How can you alter your thoughts to hold a more positive outlook?

Replace Your Thoughts with More Positive Thoughts

Change your self-talk to leave behind the "all is bad" attitude. What are the good things or silver linings that occur in a difficult relationship? What can you learn from a life challenge that equips you with knowledge and skills for dealing with difficult times?

COMBINING REALISTIC EXPECTATIONS WITH COGNITIVE REFRAMING

Changing expectations and reframing relationships are both about examining our thinking patterns. We still need to have realistic expectations as we work to reframe relationships in a more positive light. Unrealistic expectations may lead us to a positive outlook, but can also set us up for failure or disappointment.

Carmen's relationship with her sister Lily illustrates how these two strategies work together. Carmen praises Lily for her accomplishments in living well independently while managing bipolar disorder. Lily is an important and valued part of the lives of Carmen and her children. At the same time, Carmen knows that Lily could have problems with medications or stress, leading to increasing manic symptoms and possible hospitalization. She has realistic expectations about what might happen and is ready to devote attention to Lily if she needs support. Carmen's focus on the positives reduces stress in their relationship and contributes to hope for stability in their lives.

KEY CHAPTER MESSAGES

1. Family members reframed their relationship with their relative living with a mental illness to include a focus on positive aspects.

2. We may choose to end or distance ourselves from a family relationship when it becomes too harmful to sustain.

3. Family members reframed relationships by recognizing their relative's strengths.

4. Family members reframed their understanding of adverse experiences in the relationship with their relative by focusing on their own growth as an outcome.

5. Finding the silver lining in tough times decreases stress and contributes to well-being.

6. Cognitive reframing is the process of turning a negative view of a relationship, experience, or event into a more positive view.

7. Cognitive reframing leads to more positive communication with others, contributes to insight about what we experience, and reduces our stress level.

8. We can use cognitive reframing strategies to change negative thinking into more positive thinking:
   • Learn about thinking patterns.
   • Notice your thoughts.

- Challenge your thoughts.
- Replace your thoughts with more positive thoughts.

9. It is important to keep expectations realistic in the process of cognitive reframing.

Chapter 6

PAVE THE WAY WITH EMPATHY

Empathy is "the art of stepping imaginatively into the shoes of another person, understanding their feelings and perspectives, and using that understanding to guide your actions" (Roman Krznaric, 2014).[1]

Empathy makes it possible to walk alongside someone who is in the midst of adversity. It enables us to learn about their life perspectives—what is difficult and troubling and how they hope to get through tough times. For the family members in my study, empathetic understanding improved communication with their relative and led to greater compassion for their difficulties. This chapter highlights how family members conveyed empathy for their relative living with a mental illness. Here, you will learn about using empathy to communicate more effectively with your relative.

95

PARENT STORIES

Parents deliberated about the best ways to walk alongside their adult child. They wanted to respect their child's adulthood and need for independence. However, symptoms of mental illness often meant continued dependence on parental help. This conflict and the accompanying tension made it difficult for parents to encourage independence while avoiding overprotective reactions in interactions with their adult child.

Sharon Walked Alongside Her Daughter

Sharon teaches classes about mental health in her work as a public health educator for a county health department. Although she is an expert in mental health topics, she listened to information provided by mental health providers and staff when her young adult daughter, Gabrielle, needed hospitalization for symptoms brought on by a manic episode.

> *[The discharge nurse] said, "Walk alongside her in her journey of recovery." And I did that. I literally thought of that every day because the nurse said so many young adults her age who have their first episode, diagnosed between 18 and 22, don't have an adult or caregiver walk alongside them in their journey in their recovery. I say that in my classes all the time. It's about walking alongside your loved one. Not controlling [the illness].*

96

Sharon respects her young adult daughter's need to make her own choices, yet she walks alongside Gabrielle in making life and treatment decisions. When Gabrielle experienced recurring symptoms and was evaluated in the hospital emergency room, Sharon coached her on relevant information to tell the triage staff and asked Gabrielle's permission to share information. In addition, she shared her observations with Gabrielle and suggested her medications may need to be evaluated, but left it up to her daughter to discuss with her provider.

In another example, Sharon encouraged Gabrielle's self-sufficiency in everyday life by coaching her on money management skills.

> *This is her idea—she deposits her paycheck automatically into my checking account. Every day, she will text me what she needs for the day. Sometimes she has to text me twice or three times depending on what comes up. She knows that she can't manage it alone. For example, her car payment was due today. Yesterday noon she needed $30, and I don't ask her what it's for, because it's her money. I electronically transferred her $30. We have a ledger that I bought her, and we meet every Sunday. We usually have brunch. I have to go through it with her. She's taking more responsibility and she's presenting what she spends, and if she's in the hole, what her plan's going to be. She's now presenting it to me rather than me facilitating that process.*

Sharon is grateful that Gabrielle has insight about her symptoms.

> *[Gabrielle can say] "I feel like I'm going to get manic." That is extraordinarily helpful. She can call me, and*

97

we can just talk through it. "What's your plan? When
do you see somebody on your care team? Have you
refilled your prescriptions?"

Sharon noted that walking alongside her daughter alleviates her own fears. She understands Gabrielle's perspective, which makes it possible to use a supportive, helpful approach when communicating with her daughter.

Elaine Coached Her Daughter on How to Cope with Adversity

Elaine mulled over the best ways to support her daughter Terry's independence while also coaching her to manage life challenges. Elaine and her husband live in Florida half the year, and Terry usually visits them for a week. When Elaine returns from Florida, she and Terry usually see each other every two to three weeks and will text in between. Elaine admits that from her daughter's perspective, the separation is challenging. Terry has told Elaine she "doesn't have anyone." Terry does not drive; sometimes getting places is difficult. But Elaine believes her decision to live out of state part-time will help her daughter build confidence to manage on her own.

While encouraging independence, Elaine also walks alongside her daughter by teaching her the emotional management strategies she uses to cope with adversity in her own life. Elaine experienced her parents' disappointment when she became pregnant with Terry at age 17. She divorced early in her marriage, becoming the single parent of three young children, and believed she did not handle Terry's suicide attempt as a teenager in the best way. For Elaine, the search for healing through adversity led to learning to let go of inaccurate and harmful thoughts. She taught Terry a strategy she calls "affirmation," which helps to manage stressful situations. Elaine explained,

> *I discovered that when I behaved in a way that wasn't what I desired, I punished myself. When we're not feeling good about ourselves, punishment just adds to that feeling. When I started understanding that was what was happening, I realized I needed to affirm that I'm good enough, so I taught my children this too. In this way, we can address the behavior and still feel good about ourselves.*

Elaine's affirmation strategy is consistent with self-empathy, which promotes self-understanding and compassion for times of disappointment in one's behavior. She is proud of how Terry is currently managing her life and wants to affirm her daughter's successes. While cleaning Terry's apartment together before she moved to a condo, Terry said to Elaine, "I like having you here." With these words from her daughter, Elaine felt appreciated. She effectively encouraged Terry's independence by using a "walk alongside" approach to discern how to support and communicate with her daughter.

PARTNER/SPOUSE STORIES

Both Marta and Holly faced extreme challenges during their attempts to walk alongside their ill partner. For Marta, Tim's manic episodes led to actions that threatened the couple's financial stability and a safe environment for their children. Holly's husband, Ron, continually sabotaged possibilities for recovery and ultimately decided to leave the relationship. They obtained a divorce, but later Ron wanted to remarry. At the time, Holly's granddaughter lived with her and was thriving; Ron, however, did not want the granddaughter to live with them. Holly chose to give priority to the well-being of her granddaughter. Although both Marta and Holly persisted in their attempts to help their partner, ultimately the possibility of harm to their children and grandchild led them to say no to a continued intimate relationship.

Jim Adapted to His Wife's Changing Needs

Jim developed a new pattern of being with his wife, Monica, as she learned to live with limitations imposed by her symptoms. After a successful teaching career, Monica's symptoms prevented her from working. Jim found that the rhythm in their lives changed, and he gained a new understanding of both their needs.

> *Getting in a rhythm—eventually I got to a point to more or less organize my time around what her time is...We both have an understanding that I need to be there to take care of her things, to help her. She also is understanding that I need my time. That's key. It really helps a lot.*

After they both stopped drinking, Jim missed going out with friends for a few beers. But he decided to prioritize what would be best for his wife. He talked about their relationship as a "give and take." Jim developed a sense of purpose in his life resulting from his experience with Monica.

In some ways, it's like having a kid again. You have to be there for them. You have no choice. In some ways, I think it sounds weird, but her disability and coping skills actually kind of help me become more of a responsible person. It helps you grow up a hell of a lot faster. I've had friends ask me, "How do you do it?" I have no idea, I just do. There's no science to it or anything. You just do it.

Jim developed a sensitivity to his wife's needs by walking alongside her. Consequently, he experienced greater self-regard for taking on this unexpected responsibility.

Brenda Envisioned Her Husband's Experience

After leaving home because of fears about her safety, Brenda returned to care for her husband, Don, due to concern about his ability to care for himself. She has moved past the financial loss that occurred during the escalation of his manic symptoms and now has a peaceful relationship with her husband. Although they squabble about housekeeping, they have made compromises, and Brenda copes with his obsessive-compulsive symptoms. She walks alongside Don by setting up his medications once a week and checking with him at night to make sure he has not missed any doses. She also accompanies Don to his psychiatrist appointments every three months. Once she understood the barriers he encounters in daily life, Brenda showed empathy for Don by deliberately focusing on how he experiences symptoms.

Learning to look at things through another person's eyes, like my husband, who will stay in bed for 12 hours at a time and say he's afraid to get out of bed because something can go wrong. I try to put myself in his shoes and just think about, okay, how miserable that must be, instead of saying, "Suck it up, buttercup; get moving."

SIBLING STORIES

The siblings in my study had fewer opportunities to walk alongside their ill sibling, since often the needs of the ill sibling were the responsibility of their parents, at least initially. Also, the well siblings were usually not involved in everyday interactions with their brother or sister. Despite not living together, the well siblings often found ways to walk alongside the ill sibling that validated their experiences and perspectives.

Heather Affirmed Her Brother's Steps Toward Recovery

Heather explained how past patterns of family communication made it difficult for her family to manage the stress resulting from her brother Brad's symptoms. He experienced several hospitalizations and was unable to live independently. Heather worried about the burden on her parents.

I think because my parents historically have not communicated together very well, they didn't have the tools to fall back on when the big emergency came up. We had never practiced how to communicate openly or even talk about a health crisis. In the moment,

102

it was really hard, and sometimes I felt left out of things. They were the ones really calling the hospitals or the courts or the facilities and working with them. Everything I got was secondhand. Eventually, I realized that was okay.

Heather now sees her role as listening to her brother and sharing any concerns with her parents, but it is not easy to have conversations with them. She views her family as "stoic and Midwestern" and feels they do not have the skills to talk about difficult or controversial topics. She avoids taking on the role of "protector" because it does not help. She sees herself as a resource and "anchor point." Heather's "walk alongside" strategy involves listening and "being there" for her brother by affirming steps he makes toward recovery.

Carmen Applauded Her Sister's Accomplishments

Carmen celebrates and applauds the independent life that her older sister, Lily, has achieved while managing bipolar disorder. She noted that Lily's apartment is "far enough away, so she can be her own independent self and have her life too, but close enough so I can get to her or [we can] do things together." She continues to watch for signs that Lily might be cycling in her moods. Indications of mood changes can be small, such as withdrawal or not answering the phone. Lily has some insight about her cycling moods and will usually share what she is experiencing with Carmen. On some occasions, when she waits longer to share mood changes because she is trying to hide her symptoms, Carmen is very comfortable confronting Lily and initiating "walk alongside" strategies. Carmen listens to understand her distress and then uses that understanding to support Lily in decision-making about next steps for managing symptoms.

ADULT CHILDREN STORIES

Of the adult children in my study who experienced parental mental illness during childhood, three did not have the opportunity to walk alongside their ill parent. Two adult children currently have active relationships with ill parents and found ways to walk alongside them.

Jessica Focused on Her Mother's Success

Jessica's mother, Diane, worked full time until her recent retirement. Diane restructured her life to help manage her bipolar disorder by eating a healthy diet; exercising regularly; following a schedule; taking her medication consistently; and maintaining a clean, orderly home. Jessica observed that her mother takes steps to continue her stability in daily life but wondered if her mother recognized her changing moods at times.

> *There are definitely times when I can see her acting manic versus more depressed. She uses one of those lamps [that mimics natural sunlight] in the winter months. She faithfully sits in front of her lamp every morning and reads for 30 minutes. She's very good at knowing what she needs to do to stay level, but I don't know that she necessarily knows sometimes what's going on with her. She doesn't notice she's being manic.*

Diane lives close by and Jessica sees her often—weekly or sometimes twice a week. When Diane visits, Jessica reminds her to stop doing busy activities, relax, and spend time in conversation with Jessica and her children and husband. She says to her mother,

> *"Mom, you don't have to clean everything right now. You can just sit down and talk with us." [My mom says], "Oh, no—I'm just going to do the dishes real quick. It's not a problem." No matter what house she's at, the dishes are done, so if you ever need your dishes done...*

Jessica is proud of what Diane has accomplished while living with bipolar disorder.

> *I think my mom has always lived so successfully with her bipolar disorder. Once she took her medications, she just went back to the way she was before. She went back to work. She went back to doing things around the house. She was always very funny and very jovial and active and caring. She's always been very reliable. People always say, gosh, I wish I had a mom like your mom.*

Jessica believes her mother has managed her bipolar disorder well, having effectively fulfilled roles as a mother, wife, employee, and friend. She reflected, "It made me realize that people can live really successfully if they have the support and are educated." She marveled at how, in spite of the many life adversities Diane has experienced, she has done well in life. Jessica walks alongside her mother by encouraging her to relax and affirming how well she manages her symptoms. In addition, Jessica is prepared to walk alongside her into the future as she plans for her mother's aging and financial needs.

Abby Asked About Her Mother's Perspective

Although Abby experienced the chaos of her mother Mandy's bizarre behavior and the crises of repeated hospitalizations, she connected with her mother's feelings and perspectives.

> *She'll say a lot, "I'm going to die tonight. The devil's going to kill me tonight. I know it's tonight." She's been saying this for six months, every single night. I ask, 'What does the doctor say?' She said the doctor told her, "It's really sad that [you're] having these feelings." Then, I said, "What do you think about that?"*

Abby would love to see her mom able to handle an independent life; she is using a "walk alongside" approach to listen to her and affirm realistic steps toward recovery.

EMPATHY HELPS US WALK ALONGSIDE

When family members walk alongside their relative, they are engaging in an empathetic approach, making it possible to understand their relative's perspectives and experiences. Philosopher Roman Krznaric defines empathy as "the art of stepping imaginatively into the shoes of another person, understanding their feelings and perspectives, and using that understanding to guide your actions."[1]

Helen Riess, a physician who developed an empathy training program for health professionals, identified three types of empathy: 1) emotional empathy, 2) cognitive empathy, and 3) compassion.[2]

1. *Emotional empathy* is feeling what another person feels, leading to a shared emotional response. When engaging in a shared emotional response, it is important to differentiate our emotions from another's emotions in order to maintain boundaries and avoid personal distress.

2. *Cognitive empathy* occurs when we understand another's perspective as if we were in their shoes. We see the world through another's eyes, leading to understanding of their thoughts, intentions, emotions, and desires.[2] We may not agree with the other person's expressed thoughts, but we can understand them.

3. *Compassion,* which is feeling with another and understanding their distress, inspires us to care and take action to alleviate suffering.

However, we must avoid becoming overwhelmed by our responsive emotions. In fact, it is possible to suffer "compassion fatigue" or burnout resulting from a heavy emotional investment in responding to the suffering of others. One's capacity for empathy is diminished when overwhelmed by another's suffering and our own response. Diminished empathy can be a roadblock in the journey through the mental illness maze. Riess suggests that being compassionate is most effective when we concentrate on what we can control, avoid placing others' needs over our own, and avoid enabling another's destructive behaviors.

The Science of Empathy

Brain imaging technology shows that the same neural networks activated when experiencing pain and suffering are also activated when perceiving suffering in another. Riess explains that our brains are primed to experience the pain of others. This experience helps us learn about what situations we should avoid and motivates us to help the person who is suffering. We feel good about helping another and perceive a mutual benefit of living in a community where we are not alone and engage in helping one another.

The capacity for empathy varies depending on an individual's genetic background and exposure to environments that nurture the development of an empathetic response. Role models, particularly parents, contribute to a child's development of empathy. Riess explains how parents "mirror" the child's movements and emotional state. Parents respond to the child's cues by sitting or standing in similar ways and taking on similar speech patterns. The child's worth is affirmed through the response of a parent (eye contact, facial expressions, tone of voice, and words). Empathy development is also fostered through educational and professional programs that cultivate it through experience. An example is collegiate travel abroad that exposes students to cultures and lifestyles different from their own.

BARRIERS TO EMPATHY

Krznaric identified societal barriers to empathy development that interfere with our ability to understand perspectives that differ from our own.[1] These barriers prevent us from listening with an empathetic response.

- Prejudice, similar to discrimination, leads us to demean or ignore others.
- Authority keeps us from acting by leading us to comply with a decision because that is what was done in the past.
- Distance keeps us from really knowing a person or group. It is easier to dismiss the experiences of others when they are far away.
- Denial may result when we are continually bombarded by difficult, stressful stories and circumstances. We may become psychologically exhausted and numb.

Think about these barriers from the perspective of individuals who live with a mental illness. Discrimination encourages negative stereotypes that interfere with listening and understanding another's perspective. Health professionals may be stymied by the authority built into systems of care, making it difficult to hear the perspectives of clients who are experiencing symptoms of a mental illness. Or they may be overwhelmed by the burden of listening and feel distressed by their empathetic responses to clients.

Having a cultural or ethnic background different from another's decreases the capacity to empathize with that person's experience. Since the majority of mental healthcare providers and staff are white, they may have greater difficulty making a connection with clients from different ethnic groups. To breach the gap of difference, Krznaric declares that we need to make an "imaginative leap of empathy" by experiencing the other person as a human and discovering what we share and don't share. To empathize, we need to become vulnerable and listen radically. Radical listening means that we are fully present, letting go of preconceived ideas and judgments; we consciously focus on the feelings of the other; and we work to understand the other's needs.

BUILDING YOUR EMPATHY PRACTICE

Family members may find it difficult to take a leap of empathy when exhausted by a relative's mental health crises. This is a time to cultivate self-empathy. First, acknowledge that you deserve compassion, just as others deserve compassion. Realize that making mistakes is part of the human experience, and although we are accountable for our mistakes, we are worthy of understanding.[2] Having self-empathy will increase your capacity for responding with compassion to others.

A large part of how we communicate empathy is nonverbal. Riess[2] created the acronym E.M.P.A.T.H.Y. as a tool to teach healthcare providers about empathetic communication. The keys to empathy outlined in the acronym are also useful for communicating with a relative who struggles with symptoms of a mental illness.

- *E*ye contact. We make a connection with our eyes. When you look into someone's eyes, they are more likely to feel you are truly seeing them. (However, recognize that norms for eye contact may differ across cultures.)
- *M*uscles of facial expression. We mimic the facial expressions of others. We smile when they smile, or we frown in response to another's sad face. This subconscious and automatic response of our facial muscles elicits emotions connected with muscle memory, leading to an empathetic response. Interpreting facial expressions is based on biology, and, to some extent, on social conditioning and culture. Paying attention to facial expressions will help you develop an empathetic response.

110

- **P**osture. Think about how your posture communicates that you are listening and open to what someone is saying. Positioning yourself at their level makes it possible to look into their eyes, which communicates attention and interest.
- **A**ffect. Interpret and name the emotion you are seeing in the other's facial expression. When you understand the other's emotions (frustration, anger, guilt, shame, helplessness), you can connect better with what the person is feeling and also acknowledge your own response to the emotion, which will improve communication.
- **T**one of voice. The pace, rhythm, and pitch of one's voice are often more important than the actual words one speaks. To communicate empathy, you can match the volume and pace of the person you are talking to or use a soothing voice when someone is agitated and loud. This response will help them know they are being heard.
- **H**earing the whole person. This involves active, reflective listening. We listen without judgment, trying to understand another's perspective. We set aside our own emotions and listen with openness. Empathy comes from giving someone your whole attention.
- **Y**our response. How do you feel in your interaction? What is your emotional state? Does listening attentively raise unsettling emotions for you? Understanding your response will enhance your empathetic understanding and response to another.

It is difficult to communicate empathy if your relative is yelling at you or is so agitated that they are unable to respond in a reasonable manner. In those situations, the best choice is to seek professional help for needed treatment. We may feel the fear, anxiety, and confusion our relative is feeling.[3] We need to remember that these are the feelings of our relative—we are not agreeing with their thoughts or feelings, but we can validate their emotional experience. This will help our relative feel understood.

The National Alliance on Mental Illness (NAMI) Family-to-Family curriculum offers the following guidelines for communicating empathy to our relative:[4]

- Support instead of criticizing
- Encourage instead of punishing
- Reward positive behavior and ignore negative behavior
- Recognize and accept all the person's symptoms
- Patiently encourage independent behavior
- Maintain basic expectations and healthy boundaries
- Validate the emotional content of what our relative expresses
- Have empathy for ourselves

Responding with empathy means that we focus on what our relative wants without imposing the way we would do something. Sometimes, this means we need to go more slowly in conversation, remembering to always keep our relative's goals in mind.[5] These strategies will help us walk alongside our relative through the mental illness maze and develop the empathy needed to understand their experience.

COLLABORATION IN "WALKING ALONGSIDE"

My interview with Sharon inspired this chapter's focus on "walking alongside." Sharon walked alongside her daughter, Gabrielle, by collaborating with her on recovery strategies. She focused on her daughter's goals and determined how she could best support her in reaching those goals. She considered her daughter's understanding of what was important and what she needed to do. Sharon respected Gabrielle's decisions while asking questions about her plan for managing symptoms. She affirmed Gabrielle's need for independence as a young adult. She recognized the need to walk alongside her daughter step by step by understanding her experiences and perspectives and affirming her successes along the way.

Certainly, Sharon's professional work as a mental health educator gave her a foundation for practicing empathy. She called on that experience, and, while recognizing and validating her own emotional responses, engaged in empathetic, collaborative practice in responding to her daughter's needs. Sharon listened, understood, affirmed, and was compassionate, and she effectively communicated with her daughter to offer support in recovery.

You do not need a professional background in counseling or education to communicate with empathy. By intentionally thinking about what it is like to live with your relatives' life experiences and what is important to them, you will develop your capacity for empathy.

KEY CHAPTER MESSAGES

1. Having empathy makes it possible to walk alongside your relative by understanding their feelings and perspectives.

2. Walking alongside your relative provides opportunities for meaningful, positive, and effective communication.

3. Empathy involves focusing on another's experience, leading to understanding their feelings and perspectives and taking action to alleviate pain and suffering.

4. Emotional empathy is feeling what another person feels, leading to a shared emotional response.

5. Cognitive empathy occurs when we see the world through another's eyes, leading to understanding their thoughts, intentions, emotions, and desires.

6. When encountering another's pain and suffering, compassion motivates an active response to ease that pain and suffering.

7. Self-empathy helps us to understand that we deserve understanding and compassion.

8. Empathy practices involve nonverbal communication, including **E**ye contact, **M**uscles of facial expression, **P**osture, **A**ffect, **T**one of voice, **H**earing the whole person, and **Y**our response.

9. NAMI's guidelines for promoting an empathetic response to relatives include: support instead of criticizing, encourage instead of punishing, reward positive behavior and ignore negative behavior, recognize and accept all the person's symptoms, patiently encourage independent behavior, maintain basic expectations and healthy boundaries, validate the emotional content of what our relative expresses, and have empathy for ourselves.

Chapter 7

STAND ON THE SHOULDERS
OF OTHERS

*Taking the time to build a social support network
is a wise investment not only in your mental well-being
but also in your physical health and longevity
(Mayo Clinic, 2020).*[1]

Family members in my study relied on others for support to cope with overwhelming emotions and problems brought about by a relative's mental illness. Social support is "a network of family, friends, neighbors, and community members that is available in times of need to give psychological, physical, and financial help."[2] A robust social support network is essential for solving problems encountered in the mental illness maze. As described in this chapter, the stories of the parents, partners, siblings, and adult children I interviewed reveal valuable sources of social support. In addition, this chapter identifies types of social support, explains how social support contributes to well-being, and suggests strategies for building your social support network.

PARENT STORIES

Parents sought help from support groups, where they met other parents who faced similar troubles. They learned they were not alone in the challenges they faced due to an adult child's symptoms of mental illness.

Joann Found Support from Others Who "Get It"

Joann remembers sobbing for six weeks after her son Jacob's first hospitalization. She believed she had failed because, in the past, she always successfully helped her children with their problems. She knew she needed more support and joined a Family-to-Family class offered by the National Alliance on Mental Illness (NAMI). Joann discovered she was not alone in dealing with the chaos and confusion resulting from her son's bipolar disorder symptoms and treatment.

> *You learn that you're not alone and how other people have coped and done things along the way. I have really good resources. I have really good support. I can say I'm in a way better place now than I had been six months after Jacob's first hospitalization. It has made me a stronger person...I'm surrounded by people in my groups that really understand the situation, and you don't get judged for what you share, for what you're*

going through, or if you have a blowout with your child. Nobody's going to say, "Why did you do that?" They get it. You're surrounded by people that get it.

Connie Relied on Social Services for Her Daughter

Connie and her husband sought support through a NAMI Family-to-Family class when their daughter Naomi's manic behavior made them feel unsafe. Later, they built their own support group with other parents they knew who were coping with an adult child living with a mental illness. Connie observed that her marriage became stronger as she and her husband worked together to respond to Naomi's challenges with bipolar disorder. She also sought support from her boss who, in the past, had worked in mental health; he offered to make phone calls to help her find services for her daughter. Health and social services are important supports for Naomi as well as for Connie and her husband, since these services make it possible for Naomi to live independently. Naomi receives Medicaid for health costs, a housing subsidy, and Supplemental Security Income (a federal income supplement program), which give Connie and her husband the assurance that their daughter has resources for independent living and does not need to depend entirely on her parents for those needs.

Sharon Developed Friendships with Others

For Sharon, attending the NAMI Family-to-Family class helped her manage her emotions when she realized her daughter, Gabrielle, lived with a mental illness. She described hearing stories from other parents in the class as "the saving grace." In addition, she finds support through friendships and work relationships. Her current new best friends are two mothers whose adult children live with mental illness. When Sharon went back to work following Gabrielle's hospitalization, she told others that her daughter had been hospitalized and diagnosed with bipolar disorder. Sharing her story resulted in co-workers telling their own stories about having a loved one who lives with a mental illness. Sharon also received support from mental health staff during Gabrielle's hospitalization.

> *I remember this one nurse who came in at nighttime. She sat on Gabrielle's bed, and she was just really straightforward about it and talked about the benefits of a treatment and what's realistic, including the negative side effects. We both really appreciated that. She was straight about it, but kind. It felt really respectful. Gabrielle had all the information she needed to make a decision on whether that was going to be good for her.*

PARTNER/SPOUSE STORIES

Frank and Brenda reflected on the importance of faith as a significant component of their support network.

Frank Found Support Through His Faith

For many years, Frank coped with life challenges stemming from his wife Gloria's symptoms of mental illness. Following Gloria's death five years ago, Frank continues to find support through his faith and attending church.

The good Lord has been helping me. If it wouldn't have been for that—like this morning, I went to church just because I wanted to go there. I feel very at ease now. I've got my AA [Alcoholics Anonymous] books. I can go get my prayer books. I pray every day...Church is very helpful to me. I try never to come off mad or angry or something—"Well, you should have done this." Maybe I should have. I'm only human. The Lord knows I've made plenty of mistakes in my life. I always feel like no matter what I do, the good Lord's guiding me there.

Like others in the study, Frank extolled the benefits of participating in a support group for sharing experiences and learning how to help family members living with a mental illness.

One thing I'm going to stress more than anything is that people need to find a support group of some kind if they're going through this, because if you have 10 people in a group and they all talk, you'll get 10 different ideas of what this doctor did, what kind of medicine, and how this is affecting me. Another reason you've got to join these groups is because they'll teach you to take it as it comes...Because if you know you're not doing this alone, then you got some place to go and vent.

Brenda Relied on Support Groups

Brenda also finds support through her faith. After Brenda's friend helped her find an apartment on short notice because she needed a safe place to stay away from her spouse's threatening behavior, she reflected, "There was a God thing in this. Because I have a pretty strong faith, and that's God working." She has found support through many venues, including family, friends, work, NAMI, and her AA group.

> *When everything was really crazy and I moved out of the house, I was going to more [AA] meetings than I ever went to. Because that was my family. That was my support system. Some of them have had to deal with family members, loved ones with the same problems. They were very supportive. I've maintained those relationships.*

SIBLING STORIES

Siblings relied on support from mental health organizations, including care systems and advocacy groups.

Katie Received Support from the Mental Healthcare System

Katie expressed gratitude for the support she received from mental healthcare workers when she sought help for her brother, Kevin.

> *I realize people are taking on jobs that are not easy—social workers, mental health caretakers— they didn't go into it to make money. They went into it because they cared and wanted to make a*

difference...Because it's not an easy job. I feel, for the most part, anytime I have called to get Kevin help, we've been helped. We've had people who seem like they legitimately care. We've always gotten the help we need from social services. Part of it is because my brother and my mom live in a small town. People know them—the police, social services, people who run group homes. They know Kevin struggles, and they want to help. I've always had positive experiences, and I think part of that is because of my attitude and reverence toward people who have chosen this career path.

Dick Found Support Through Teaching NAMI Classes

When Dick became the primary caregiver for his brother, Stuart, he looked for support groups. Later, he learned about NAMI and started going to classes offered by the organization. Now he has access to resources, teaches a NAMI Family-to-Family class, and finds it helpful to talk with others who have similar experiences.

Every class that I'm an instructor, I tell them, "You might think I'm doing this for you. I'm not. I'm doing it for myself." If you really want to learn a subject, teach it. That's what I get out of it. The more that I learn about mental illness and the treatment of mental illness and coping strategies, [it] helps me deal with it better.

ADULT CHILDREN STORIES

Only one of the five adult children in the study participated in therapy while growing up to help deal with emotions related to parental mental illness.

As an Adult, Mark Found Support Through Therapy

Mark did not experience the benefits of therapy until he became an adult. During his childhood, he had no one he could talk to about his experiences with his father. Mark's mother was the only one who told him he was a good person. He wishes he could have heard the message about being a good person sooner in his life. He explained that when he was growing up, getting therapy was viewed as a weakness and meant that something was wrong. When counseling later became available to him through his job, he seized the opportunity, which helped him develop positive self-esteem. He continues to go for short periods of counseling to "spill my guts again to feel better about things." Mark is now comfortable seeking support in a confidential, professional counseling environment.

Abby Received Support from Her Family

At the time of the interviews, Abby and her family were in the midst of determining how to best respond to her mother Mandy's mental health needs. The family came together to support one another in decision-making. Abby's father and husband both supported her decision to visit Mandy less often in the hospital in order to reduce the added stress in her life. She explained,

> *You definitely need someone to help you realize, "I need to take care of me." It's hard to say that to yourself. When someone else says it, you're okay, I can see that. [My father] has been a really big source of strength for me.*

WHAT IS SOCIAL SUPPORT?

When family members relied on others during difficult times, they learned they were not alone. They learned about coping strategies, treatment options, and social service resources that others in similar situations found helpful. They became more realistic about expectations for their relative's recovery and their own role in supporting that recovery. They relied on existing social support networks of family, friends, and work and community relationships. They found additional social support through community classes and support groups for family members.

Social support is a broad term that includes a variety of support sources and different kinds of help or assistance. We can think of social support as encompassing four major types:[3]

- *Appraisal support* involves affirming statements or actions that contribute to feeling good about oneself.
- *Emotional support* contributes to feeling liked, admired, respected, or loved.
- *Informational support* is the provision of knowledge during times of stress that contributes to problem-solving.

- *Instrumental support* is the provision of tangible aid, goods, or services.

For example, a family member who attends a support group receives appraisal support when the leader or another group member says they are glad to see them there. In classes for family members, participants experience appraisal support when they receive a certificate of class completion; they are being affirmed for their time and investment in class sessions. Emotional support occurs when a group listens to a participant's story and acknowledges their distress, leading to feelings of being heard and respected. Informational support is experienced by family members who attend support groups and classes as they learn about resources and programs available to them and their relative. Family members benefit from the instrumental support provided to their relative through mental health programs and services like income support, employment support, housing support, crisis services, and community mental health services.

HOW DOES SOCIAL SUPPORT HELP?

Social support helps us cope with difficult situations that increase our stress levels. It protects against the negative effects of stress.[3] We look to our social network for encouragement of healthy behaviors. For example, when Joann was severely stressed by her son's manic symptoms and hospitalization, her sister encouraged her to keep her weekly fitness schedule at the gym. In addition, social support promotes a positive psychological outlook by contributing to stability, a sense of purpose, and a feeling of belonging.

Social support makes us more resilient to stress. Studies show that persons with a low level of social support have higher levels of stress reactivity as measured by an elevated heart rate and increased blood pressure.[4] Studies on the benefits of family support programs show positive outcomes for family members and their relatives who live with a mental illness. Benefits for family members include improved coping skills, increased empathy for their relative, fewer concerns about their relative's future, and relief that they are not alone in their experience.[5] They may also grow personally through developing self-confidence, recognizing inner strengths, becoming closer to God and family, learning to do new things, and making new friends.[6] When individuals living with a mental illness participated in a mental health clubhouse, which provides socialization and recovery services, benefits for the individual's entire family included decreased family burden and stress, improved family communication and relationships, and a greater sense of hope. In the clubhouse model, participants have access to emotional and instrumental support through clubhouse activities, and they have opportunities to develop independence, skills for living, and friendships.[7]

BUILDING YOUR SOCIAL SUPPORT NETWORK

Mayo Clinic[1] and the American Psychological Association[8] offer the following suggestions for strengthening your social support network.

Take a Class

Community or college classes on your special interests or hobbies will connect you with others who have similar interests. Classes specific to mental health topics will connect you with others who are navigating the complex world of mental illness in their search for help. Family members in my study who completed the NAMI Family-to-Family class received emotional and informational support through their interactions with other class participants.

Volunteer

Although you may feel overwhelmed by current life responsibilities, volunteering will bring you into contact with others who have similar values and interests. These connections take your mind off the stressors in your life, lighten your mood, and make you feel valued by others (appraisal support). Family members in the study who were frustrated with their failure to fix their relative's situation found volunteering to be rewarding when they discovered their capacity to contribute to the well-being of others.

Invite Others to Fitness Activities

Fitness clubs and exercise activities at community centers offer a great social support source of new friends who also value getting regular exercise. Invite friends for a walk or exercise activity, which will provide you with additional social connection and the opportunity for emotional support as you share life experiences.

Seek Peer Support

Family members who joined a family support group received emotional and informational support and discovered that others were in similar situations. They also received validation (appraisal support) for the distress and emotions they were going through.

Be Proactive

You have to make the effort and take the time to connect with others. Don't expect people to come to you. In making the effort to reach out to family and friends and participate in community events, you will likely feel a sense of accomplishment and find meaningful connections.

Explore Online Resources

Although face-to-face interactions are the most beneficial (according to research), social networking sites offer the opportunity to communicate across distance and can bring together people who share similar experiences. Be sure to evaluate the credibility and confidentiality of social networking sites. Mental health organization websites are good resources for informational support, but again, be sure to evaluate credibility. As noted in Chapter 2, some of the best organizations for accurate information on mental health are the American Psychiatric Association, the Centers for Disease Control and Prevention, Mayo Clinic, NAMI, and the National Institute of Mental Health.

Ask for Help

Look to places in your community that can offer connection possibilities. These include places of worship, community centers, schools, libraries, and local branches of national organizations. Local newspapers are a good source of information about groups and programs in the community.

HOW TO NURTURE YOUR SOCIAL SUPPORT NETWORK

We also need to pay attention to what we can do to actively sustain our social support network. This means being aware of how we can provide social support to others. Mayo Clinic[1] offers these suggestions for nurturing relationships in our social network:

- Stay in touch. Initiate and answer phone calls, return emails, and reciprocate invitations.
- Don't compete. Celebrate the success of others.
- Be a good listener. Listen to discern what is important to another.
- Don't overdo it. Establish consistent contact, but avoid overwhelming others with phone calls and email messages.
- Appreciate your friends and family. Be sure to say thank you and tell them they are important to you.
- Give back. Find ways to provide support to others.

SOCIAL SUPPORT AS AN ESSENTIAL COPING STRATEGY

Although initially you might be reluctant to talk about your relative's mental illness because of shame or a fear of discrimination, accepting social support from others is vitally important for coping effectively with overwhelming emotions. For several adult children in the study, lacking social support during their childhood experience with a parent's mental illness contributed to challenges in adulthood. This lack of support stemmed from the typical view in the past that talking about mental illness was taboo—a view that was compounded by the lack of available counseling or the perception that seeking counseling meant you were "weak."

Jessica's mother had the foresight to seek family counseling during her daughter's growing up years, which provided needed social support. For Jessica, counseling contributed to effective coping and positive views about her mother and their current mother-daughter relationship. For Mark, little support other than from his mother was available to him during his childhood and teen years. He remembers feeling angry and isolated because of his father's mental illness and only in adulthood had the opportunity for counseling. Sam struggled with relationships in response to challenges in his youth related to his mother's mental illness and suicide. However, after Mark and Sam examined their past parental relationships and the resulting impact on their lives, they were able to find rewarding and satisfying relationships. Abby, as a young adult who is currently experiencing distress related to her mother's symptoms, is surrounded by supportive family members who are all willing to talk about their emotions. The social support networks of the family members I interviewed help them cope more effectively with the stressors brought about by their relative's symptoms and make it possible for them to move forward in their journey through the mental illness maze.

Since many of the family members who shared their stories already had a connection with NAMI through support groups, family classes, or other events, it is not surprising that they found these activities to be an important source of social support. Upon hearing the stories of others in similar situations, they openly talked about their own experiences and were able to know that someone cared. Their expanded social support network made it possible for them to see hope for both themselves and their relative. They were no longer alone in their journey and now have others they can rely on.

KEY CHAPTER MESSAGES

1. Social support is "a network of family, friends, neighbors, and community members that is available in times of need to give psychological, physical, and financial help."[2]

2. Social supports for family members included a variety of sources: faith and church, other family members, work relationships, friends, mental health staff and providers, and support groups and classes for family members (e.g., NAMI, AA).

3. Support available to individuals living with a mental illness, such as mental health programs, Social Security disability benefits, food support programs, employment support, and Medicaid for healthcare, are also important sources of support for family members. These supports relieve family members of the added burden of responsibility to help their relative meet basic needs.

4. Family members benefitted from the following types of social support:
   - *Appraisal support*, which involves affirming statements or actions that contribute to feeling good about oneself.
   - *Emotional support*, which contributes to feeling liked, admired, respected, or loved.
   - *Informational support*, the provision of knowledge during times of stress that contributes to problem-solving.
   - *Instrumental support*, the provision of tangible aid, goods, or services.

5. Social support protects against the negative effects of stress and contributes to a more positive outlook on life.

6. Research confirms that participation in family support programs is beneficial to family members who have a relative living with a mental illness. Benefits include improved coping skills, increased self-confidence, greater sensitivity to persons with disabilities, recognition of strengths, and becoming closer to family.

7. Choose from a menu of strategies to build your social support network: take a class, volunteer, invite others to fitness activities, seek out peer support, be proactive, explore online resources, and ask for help.

8. Credible sources of informational support include the following organizations:
    *   American Psychiatric Association
        https://www.psychiatry.org/patients-families
    *   Centers for Disease Control and Prevention
        https://www.cdc.gov/mentalhealth/learn/
    *   Mayo Clinic
        **https://www.mayoclinic.org/diseases-conditions/
        mental-illness/symptoms-causes/syc-20374968**
    *   National Alliance on Mental Illness
        **https://www.nami.org/Learn-More/
        Mental-Health-Conditions**
    *   National Institute of Mental Health
        https://www.nimh.nih.gov/health/topics/index.shtml

9. Nurture your social support network by staying in touch, avoiding competition, listening carefully, not overwhelming

others with phone calls and emails, expressing your appreciation, and providing support to others.

10. Be open to sharing your story and listening to the stories of others.

Chapter 8

FIND RESILIENCE, KEEP GOING

*Resilience is the process of adapting well in the
face of adversity, trauma, tragedy, threats or
significant sources of **stress**—such as family and
relationship problems, serious health problems, or
workplace and financial stressors
(American Psychological Association, 2020).[1]*

As the family members in my study adjusted to changes resulting from their relative's symptoms of mental illness, they bounced back from adversity and persevered. Without a doubt, these family members were resilient. This chapter explores factors that help us become more resilient and provides examples of resiliency from the stories of family members. Resilience keeps us going on our journey through the mental illness maze.

FACTORS LEADING TO RESILIENCE

Symptoms of mental illness in a relative are a significant source of stress. Resilience will strengthen your ability to cope more effectively with the challenges resulting from your relative's symptoms. In their book *The Science of Mastering Life's Greatest Challenges*, Steven Southwick and Dennis Charney discussed the following 10 factors that promote resilience:[2]

- Realistic optimism
- Facing fear
- Moral compass
- Religion and spirituality
- Social support
- Resilient role models
- Physical fitness
- Brain fitness
- Cognitive and emotional flexibility
- Meaning and purpose

Which of these factors are already part of your life habits? What actions do you need to take to develop greater resiliency? While some individuals have personality characteristics that are consistent with resilience, everyone can develop viewpoints and habits that promote a resilient approach to life. Consider how each of these factors contributes to resiliency.

Realistic Optimism

Optimists have the ability to reappraise negative situations in order to find a more positive outlook. When confronted with adversity, an optimistic person engages in problem-solving and tends to view life as meaningful. To nurture optimism, focus on positive thinking and say no to negative thinking.

Facing Fear

Fear is an adaptive response to potential danger. Your brain prepares you to act, also known as a "fight or flight" response. You may be conditioned to respond with fear because of a previous adverse experience; however, you can learn to face your fears by understanding them and choosing strategies to diminish them. Viewing fear as a guide will sharpen your focus and help you make better decisions. Fear can be used as an opportunity to learn new coping strategies and adapt. Think about what you fear and how others manage fear. Work on specific skills to help overcome fear, such as reflecting on your experience of fear or focusing on deep breathing to relax. You can recruit others to help you manage fear, including friends or colleagues, members of a spiritual or faith-based group, or counselors.[1] Understand that fear is normal, and that learning how to channel it and reduce it will contribute to greater resiliency.

Moral Compass

Moral compass refers to living by ethical principles and having conviction about doing the right thing. Think about how the following statements apply to how you make decisions.[3]

- I stay true to myself even when I'm afraid to do so.
- My deeply held values guide my choices.
- I make decisions that are consistent with my beliefs.
- I can handle unpleasant feelings.
- Even if I don't feel like it, I do what I need to do.

When you stay true to your moral compass, you are likely to make better decisions that contribute to well-being for both you and your relative.

Religion and Spirituality

Research shows there is a connection between the active practice of religious faith and physical and mental health.[2] The practice of prayer contributes to a sense of well-being, positive self-esteem, and optimism. Researchers found that specific types of prayer contribute to well-being: prayers of adoration, which focus on worshiping God without specific requests; thanksgiving prayers; and prayers of reception, which foster closeness with God.[4] The comfort and assurance generated from faith practices contribute to resiliency.

Social Support

Both the giving and receiving of social support contribute to resiliency. A strong social support network will help you flourish even in the midst of adversity. Chapter 7 explains the value of social support for family members who endeavor to assist a relative living with a mental illness.

Resilient Role Models

We admire role models of resilience for their strength, determination, perseverance, and accomplishments. Role models inspire us to be like them. They come from all parts of life and could be a parent, a grandparent, a teacher, a coach, a survivor of adversity, or someone famous. We learn about resiliency by observing our role models. Of course, role models are not perfect in all they do, but we can focus on the characteristics and actions that led to their accomplishments. We observe others, focus on those characteristics and actions we admire, and practice the attitude or action we have observed that is consistent with resilience. Then we can reflect on how our actions help us understand and manage adversity. Who is your role model for resiliency? What attitudes or actions do you admire that you would like to integrate into your response to life challenges?

Physical Fitness

Exercise is a choice that results in many benefits, including mood improvement, weight management, better sleep, increased energy, and better management of chronic diseases.[2] When feeling overwhelmed, you may find it difficult to begin an exercise program or fit it into an already busy day. A key strategy is to develop a pattern of physical exercise by building it into your schedule. Exercising with a friend can be both motivating and fun. Regular exercise contributes to resiliency by giving you more energy to tackle the challenges of the day.

Brain Fitness

Your brain helps you regulate emotions. Emotions may overwhelm you during your relative's times of symptom escalation and crisis. You can train your brain to regulate emotions by meditating or doing mindfulness activities. Another way to regulate emotions is through cognitive behavioral therapy (CBT), which can benefit both family members and their relative living with a mental illness. CBT teaches individuals how to examine thoughts that influence feelings and actions. It helps individuals check their thoughts against reality and decide whether their response is unreasonable or reasonable. Conducting a reality check may lead to a behavior change and better management of a stressful situation.

Cognitive and Emotional Flexibility

When surprised by unexpected adverse events, resilient individuals have greater flexibility in their thinking and emotional responses. They are less likely to fall apart or feel stuck in the situation. They come up with new ideas for managing their emotions and generate possible approaches for assisting their relative.

If needed, they call on supporters for ideas and help in tackling a problem.

Your flexibility is enhanced when you accept what you cannot change and realize there are alternatives to coping strategies that are not working. Along with acceptance, you can also reappraise how you are viewing the situation and revise your outlook and responses. The following guidelines are useful for reappraising a difficult situation.[2]

- Fully describe the stressful situation.
- Ask how the situation could be worse.
- Ask how the situation could be better.
- Create a story about a worse version.
- Create a story about a better version.
- Think about what you can do to create a better version and decrease the likelihood of a worse version.
- Place the situation into perspective.

Sometimes, gaining distance from a difficult situation through reappraisal results in a clearer perspective on what is needed to improve or resolve the situation.

Meaning and Purpose

It is possible to find meaning and purpose in adversity and meaning in your own personal growth as you discover inner strengths. You may develop a stronger connection with your relative and find more compassion as you increase your knowledge about the symptoms and treatment of mental illness. To explore meaning and purpose when experiencing tough times, consider these questions: 1)

What is the meaning of the adversity you are experiencing? 2) What can you do to have a positive outlook? and 3) How do you find the truth in the situation? Reflecting on these questions will help you to focus on your inner life, identify strengths, and find purpose in your life, all of which contribute to resiliency.

FAMILY AND COMMUNITY RESILIENCY

Family interactions have the potential to contribute to resilient family life even in the midst of adverse events. Although mental illness in a relative may lead to unpredictability, resilience is demonstrated in established family routines, connectedness that involves humor and gathering together, and availability of support networks.[4] Yet, it is important to be vigilant about symptoms and crises an ill relative might experience. Researchers suggest that open communication about a parent's mental illness contributes to resiliency in families, while shame may interfere with family resiliency because it prevents the sharing of feelings.[5]

Protective factors in the community also promote resiliency, including access to mental health services, community support, feeling connected to the community, and having strong extended family and other social networks.[4] In addition, our own resilience motivates us to advocate for the creation of programs and environments that promote resiliency for others who live in our community.[2,6]

WE DON'T FEEL RESILIENT EVERY DAY

Resiliency means holding on to your values in making decisions, dealing with unpleasant feelings, and doing what you need to do even if you don't feel like it.[3] The everyday decisions we make as we respond to difficult life events and adversity lead to a pattern of being resilient. Resiliency is about persevering during tough times and being committed to intentionally deciding how to manage the challenges we encounter every day. However, resilience is not a steady state from day to day. When we have low-energy days or are coping with many stressors at once, we will benefit from taking a break and realizing that our inner strength will return and enable us to manage the situation.

RESILIENCE WHILE LIVING WITH A MENTAL ILLNESS

Your relative's state of resilience will vary from day to day depending on life circumstances, moods, and medications. To learn more about the meaning of resilience for someone who lives with symptoms of a mental illness, I interviewed Lynn, who I met through mental health advocacy work, about her pathway to resilience. Lynn has lived with bipolar disorder for over 30 years and successfully manages her symptoms. She has many protective factors contributing to her resiliency, including a sister who values their relationship, a rewarding part-time job, and a social network in the apartment complex where she resides. She described how she needed to overcome the shame and stigma of stressful experiences connected with her manic symptoms. Initially, she found it difficult to be open about her bipolar disorder, but then she realized she could use her knowledge and experience to support others. She is now a peer advocate for others who live with a mental illness.

As she moved from a successful career to learning to live with fewer economic resources, Lynn discovered she needed to accept what had occurred in the past and acknowledge the embarrassment and shame that accompanied her changed life circumstances. Accepting the possibility of having another manic episode became a part of her resilience repertoire. Lynn balances the recognition that her illness affects her daily life with realistic optimism about what may happen in the future. Lynn is resilient.

STORIES OF RESILIENCE

All the family members I interviewed demonstrated resilience. Participants found purpose by telling their story to help others in similar situations. In the midst of adversity, they used a problem-solving approach. They increased their knowledge and reached out for support as they experienced overwhelming emotions in response to their relative's mental illness. Their actions model resiliency.

A Focus on Wellness

All participants strengthened their self-care, and several focus on wellness in their careers. Elaine, a parent of a daughter living with bipolar disorder, teaches classes for an organization that supports complementary healing strategies. She also participates in meditation retreats. Elaine is doing work that is consistent with her philosophy about the importance of the mind-body connection and the interaction between physical and emotional well-being. She is excited about how her work helps people. Janet, whose brother lives with a mental illness, contributes to The Center for Mind-Body Medicine initiatives; her participation builds her resilience. She explained how group support, deep belly breathing, movement, imagery, drawing, and forgiveness meditation are powerful self-care strategies for promoting mental health. She spoke about the benefits of group support and how mental health professionals also need support to keep burnout at bay.

Taking Responsibility for What Is Possible to Control

Elaine, whose daughter attempted suicide in the past, tries to avoid responding out of guilt or fear in her relationship with her daughter. She reflected about her responsibility.

> *Because she didn't commit suicide, I don't want to take her success. It's hers. I think that is an important part of parenting. We have an impact, yet how do you let them do what they need to do? Because that would be too much for anyone to take someone else's behavior and say that if [they tried] to commit suicide, it's my fault or my responsibility. I think that's part of mental health—what is my responsibility, what's yours? Because you interact, and there's that whole piece when you think that you're in control of somebody else; I think that's similar to the alcoholism. What I experienced with my ex-husband is that you're not responsible for that.*

Marta, who acted to distance herself and her children from her partner's threatening behavior, demonstrated resilience by putting her energy into her work and caring for her children. She showed flexibility and purpose through prioritizing her actions to keep the family safe.

Relying on Faith

Frank and Brenda had partners who lived with a mental illness, and Katie's brother lived with severe and persistent mental illness. They spoke about the importance of having faith in God and experienced reassurance that God cared for them, even in the face of adversity.

Openness in Talking About Mental Illness

Abby's family members, who faced a series of mental illness crises with her mother, demonstrate resiliency when they talk with one another about best treatment strategies. They have strong family connections that sustain them through adversity. Jessica, whose mother has found stability in managing symptoms, talks to her about any changing moods she observes. Connie, who experienced the adversity of her daughter's crises with potentially harmful symptoms, openly confronts her daughter about escalating symptoms while offering support to manage those symptoms.

Finding New Purpose

Anita channeled her overwhelming emotions by creating art that gave meaning to her daughter's upsetting symptoms of mental illness. She also found purpose by advocating for neglected and abused children's best interests in the court system as a guardian ad litem volunteer. Heather, whose brother and husband both live with a mental illness, channels her energy into advocacy activities.

She wrote letters on mental health to magazine editors, two of which were published, and participated in National Alliance on Mental Illness advocacy activities. Sam demonstrates his dedication to individuals living with a mental illness through his career as a county mental health social worker.

An Attitude of Optimism

Carmen applauds her sister's accomplishments and expresses gratitude for their relationship. She also acknowledges that her sister's symptoms may call her into action to support her in the future. Frank, whose family adversity included his wife's mental illness, can look back on the past and find humor in family events. He now focuses on his wife's stability in her later years and remembers how much his family loved her. Sharon is optimistic about her daughter's ability to live independently with family and community support. Although her daughter's mental health condition limits her educational and career aspirations, Sharon accepts that reality and is grateful her daughter found meaningful work.

ADDITIONAL TIPS TO BUILD RESILIENCE

Mayo Clinic[7] offers concise strategies you can use to become more resilient. In addition to connecting with support and taking care of yourself, consider these actions.

- *Make every day meaningful.* Think of something to do that provides a sense of accomplishment and purpose. Set goals that provide meaning for the future.

- *Learn from experience.* Reflect on how you have managed adversity in the past and what helped you through tough times.
- *Remain hopeful.* Accept what has occurred and anticipate how you can adapt to challenges.
- *Be proactive.* Do not ignore problems, thinking they might go away. Adopt a problem-solving approach and know that you can improve your situation.

KEY CHAPTER MESSAGES

1. Resilience helps us cope with adversity and stressful life situations.

2. Factors that contribute to the development of resiliency are:
   - Realistic optimism
   - Facing fear
   - Moral compass
   - Religion and spirituality
   - Social support
   - Resilient role models
   - Physical fitness
   - Brain fitness
   - Cognitive and emotional flexibility
   - Meaning and purpose

3. Protective factors that contribute to family resiliency include the presence of routines in the context of unpredictability of parent illness, family connectedness involving humor and gathering together, and helpful support networks.

4. Community factors such as access to mental health services, community support, feeling connected to the community, and strong extended family and other social networks contribute to resiliency for individuals who live with a mental illness.

5. When you have low energy or are coping with many stressors at once, it may be helpful to take a break and realize

that your sense of resiliency will return. You will soon find your inner strength and the perspective that will enable you to manage the challenge.

6. Individuals who live with a mental illness have the capacity to develop a resilient approach to life that contributes to greater stability.

7. Key resiliency actions of family members interviewed for this study were:
   - A focus on wellness
   - Taking responsibility for what is possible to control
   - Relying on faith
   - Openness in talking about mental illness
   - Finding new purpose
   - An attitude of optimism

8. Mayo Clinic offers six tips for becoming more resilient.
   - Get connected for support
   - Take care of yourself
   - Make every day meaningful
   - Learn from experience
   - Remain hopeful
   - Be proactive

Chapter 9

NURTURE HOPE TO
SEE WHAT'S POSSIBLE

*Realistic hope is an active process with the intent
and possibility of fulfilment and an assessment of
what can and what cannot be changed
(Thaïs Helène Downman, 2008).*[1]

A year ago, Anita agonized about how to help her two young adult daughters, Serena and Nina, who both live with a serious mental illness. Anita's therapist asked how she was doing now that the "hope phase" was over. For Anita, the therapist's question implied that she shouldn't be hopeful and intensified her distress about her daughters' symptoms and what the future might bring. With great uncertainty about the prognosis for her daughters, Anita felt "tricked by hope." How is it possible for Anita to find hope when her life with her daughters is so difficult? What is the role of mental healthcare providers in encouraging hope? This chapter will feature family member stories of finding hope, explore the meaning of hope and hope interventions, and offer strategies for collaborating with mental healthcare professionals in promoting hope for recovery for a relative living with a mental illness.

Hope helps us look forward to a better future, but at the same time we may be fearful of being disappointed when what we hope for does not happen. When first confronted by our relative's symptoms of mental illness, we hope the symptoms will go away and never return. Although some who are diagnosed with a mental illness do find effective treatment and learn to manage their symptoms, others struggle with repeated episodes of mania, depression, and/or psychosis. Our hope is battered when we continue to see our relative face repeated episodes and hospitalizations. Family members in my study found they needed to change their hope outlook for their relative by viewing hope as possibilities rather than expectations.

PARENT STORIES

Anita Found Hope in Living One Day at a Time

Anita reflected on her therapist's question about the loss of hope.

> *I went home thinking, there's a phase like hope? I don't think she meant to say that. But I made this sculpture of a girl holding an axe with an egg on a tree stump, and it's called "F___ Hope." It was painful to think that I was being, like, tricked by hope.*

Here, have some hope. That will help you get through this. Sprinkle on hope for you. That was rough.

When asked about how she thinks about hope now, Anita responded,

I don't know. I just kind of go one day at a time. There's hope in that. I'm thinking maybe tomorrow will be different. Day after day. It's so hard not to think ahead, it really is. How long is Nina going to be in psychosis? She's not doing the right medications. Right now, she takes them a few at a time or a lot at a time. She's 21 and we can't do anything. What does this look like for [my husband] and me? We had dreams of our kids being independent.

Elaine Hopes for a Better Relationship with Her Daughter

Elaine, whose adult daughter, Terry, lives independently and takes medication for bipolar disorder, is proud of how Terry is currently managing her life. She wishes to affirm her daughter's successes. As Terry gets older, Elaine hopes that Terry will find "a path that she's comfortable with and can sustain." She observed that Terry is "doing the best she can and what she thinks is right." Elaine hopes that her daughter will find a life partner. She would love to see someone in Terry's life who cares for her, and she is hopeful that their mother-daughter relationship will continue to grow in positive ways. She is realistic about expecting outcomes for Terry that are within the realm of possibility.

If you expect a different result than what you're getting right now, you're in for a rude awakening. [You need] to be able to really have compassion for what's happened in the past and have some hope.

Joann Focuses on Hope for Good Family Times

Joann wants other parents of young adults living with a mental illness to know that it will get better and there is hope. In support groups, she learned that although mental illness can be challenging, families are doing fine. Life goes on; they are able to lead good lives. She observed, "It was just really lovely to hear in every story [that] there are good times." Her outlook focuses on both the hopeful possibilities and the reality of mental illness.

You're going to have good times and you're going to have bad times. And you know what? You may be blessed and have a really good recovery after that and move forward. But it's not the same for everybody, and I think that is important to share. Even though the mental illness diagnosis may be bipolar, how they experience their illness is not the same.

Joann feels less alone when she shares her experience with others. Although she has hope that things will get better, she tempers a hopeful outlook with the realization that she is on a lifelong journey in supporting her son, Jacob, and taking care of herself.

PARTNER/SPOUSE STORIES

Marta Hopes for Her Partner's Recovery

Marta is hopeful that Tim will get his life "under control," yet she recognizes the reality that her former partner lives with a serious mental illness. Although the chaos of Tim's illness resulted in a separation and move, she would like to see him get the help he needs. When Tim ended up in court, Marta wrote a letter to the court to clarify what he needed, acknowledging his strengths and revealing her hope for his recovery. She wrote,

> He is an intelligent, talented, witty, and caring man... He shared in providing for our family over the years and raising our two children and shared in their interests and achievements...My wishes and what I believe would be in his best interest going forward: There needs to be treatment. I believe he needs inpatient treatment for the chemical dependency and follow-up with a support group to continue sobriety, a continued program to assist with assuring that medications are being taken and support for the mental illness, a fathers' and children's support group to help heal the relationship between him and his children, and a back-to-work program or a support system that can give him the skills to support himself.

Marta hopes that Tim will focus on what will help him become stable. At this point in her journey, she turns to hope for peace in her life and the capability to support her children in getting "to the levels of where they need to be in their life." Marta has persevered with realistic hope through tough times.

SIBLING STORIES

Katie Found Realistic Hope

Katie reflected about the severity of her brother Kevin's mental illness and repeated hospitalizations. She has become more realistic about possibilities for him.

> *Have hope, but also realize you're going to have to come up with a way to cope. That includes being open about how you feel, feeling feelings, and not shutting them out like I did. Try to do what you can, but realize you can't be a martyr and you're not going to save anyone. When I was going through my journey, I had no one early on at all. I think at that time, I was like, "I'm smart, I'm young, I can do anything, I know everything." Look, you have to have a lot of self-love. Therapy is important, and you've got to be realistic with what you can give.*

For Katie, letting go of her perceived responsibility that she needed to find the solution for Kevin's mental illness, engaging in therapy, and getting educated about mental illness all led to finding realistic hope.

Dick Focuses on What Is Possible for His Brother

Dick hopes that his brother, Stuart, "can find that happy place between depression and mania." Currently, he wants to see Stuart, who lives independently, become less depressed and sleep fewer hours each day. He realizes that his brother does better in comparison to many other individuals. As Stuart's primary caregiver, Dick continues to experience the burden and concerns associated with his responsibility for his brother. Although he expresses ambivalence about caring for Stuart and monitoring his symptoms and treatment, the brothers' relationship has become closer. Dick now understands that some characteristics, such as being obstinate and irritable, are a part of bipolar disorder. Although saddened by Stuart's life limitations due to mental illness symptoms, he is realistic about what is possible for his brother and channels his hope into helping others by volunteering for the National Alliance on Mental Illness (NAMI).

ADULT CHILDREN STORIES

Jessica Realizes the Future for Her Mother May Change

Jessica is hopeful that her mother Diane's medication will remain effective and that she will "continue to live with this disorder successfully and healthy and happy." She also knows her mother may need more help as she ages, so she is realistic about changes that might occur in the future.

Abby Hopes for Stability for Her Mother

When Abby's mother, Mandy, went through a series of hospitalizations due to unresolved symptoms of mental illness, she wondered if visiting her more often would help her get better faster. In retrospect, Abby realized, "My mother needed more help than we could provide." Abby now knows Mandy's illness will not go away, but she is hopeful that programs and medications can help her mother find a stable and satisfying life. She acknowledged the reality of changed relationships within her family resulting from Mandy's many recent mental health crises. In the future, Abby hopes some of her family members will participate in classes for families to learn more about mental illness and how to support their relative.

THE MEANING OF HOPE

Hope has to be able to name and confront fears as well. True hope is not putting blinders on and pretending that everything is okay when it's not. But it's the faith to move forward and trust, despite what is otherwise concerning to us (Jon Pederson, 2018).[2]

Hope is future-oriented. In hoping, we expect to reach a goal that we value. Hope motivates the person living with a mental illness to find meaning and purpose in life while managing symptoms. Hope leads to focusing on one's strengths rather than getting bogged down with negative self-views. It boosts positive emotions and behaviors that contribute to recovery.[3] For hope to play a role in moving toward recovery, it is important to choose goals that are realistic and achievable.[4]

Hope involves considering future possibilities and the consequences of these possibilities.[1] We make judgments about what we believe should happen and then promote the fulfillment of that hope. However, if we do not consider what can be changed and what is not possible to change, unrealistic hope will likely lead to frustration, disappointment, rage, despair, and finally apathy. At that point, there is loss of motivation and energy to maintain the hope.[5]

Two processes are required in order for hope to motivate attitudes and actions toward achieving a future goal.[5] First, you must desire the goal and believe that it can be accomplished. Second, you need to identify possible alternative strategies for reaching that goal. It is helpful to choose "benchmarks" or measures that show evidence of working toward the goal. Also, the uncertainty you might have about achieving a goal will help you consider different pathways or strategies and reassess what is realistic.[6]

EVIDENCE ABOUT THE BENEFITS OF HOPE

Researchers have found many emotional and physical health benefits of having a hopeful attitude.[5,6] Hopeful people:

- Are more likely to be resilient and flourish
- Can identify productive paths to reach a goal
- Are less reactive to stressful situations
- Have a higher level of life satisfaction and a sense of purpose
- Are better able to cope with illness and difficult situations

Hope contributes to our physical and psychosocial well-being, helps us cope with loss and grief, alleviates uncertainty, and is associated with decreased burden among caregivers.

Over time, loss of hope for an unrealistic goal will prompt family members to adjust their outlook and develop a more realistic hope. Initially, when confronted with a relative's mental illness diagnosis, family members may hope for a full recovery; this hope protects them from the devastation of acknowledging the possibility of long-term limitations for their relative. As family members let go of the expectation for a full recovery, they are able to find a more limited, realistic hope for what is possible for their relative.[7]

HOPE AS AN INTERVENTION

Encouragers of hope for a relative living with a mental illness include family and friends, mental health professionals, the relative's religious beliefs, and keeping a positive attitude.[7] As a family member, you can nurture in your relative a hopeful attitude that is also realistic by affirming choices that will contribute to their recovery, identifying alternative strategies for reaching their goals as well as potential barriers, and focusing on their meaning of success.[5] You can encourage your relative's hope for better symptom management and stability in life. Think about hope as an intervention. The following five interventions can encourage hope in people living with a serious mental illness:[8]

1. Collaborate on strategies for illness management. This means including goals for recovery desired by the person living with a mental illness. Family members can

emphasize inclusion of their relative's preferences in the recovery plan. Illness management incorporates education on the illness, finding medications that work, controlling symptoms, and creating a treatment plan fine-tuned to the individual's unique needs.

2. Encourage positive relationships that communicate hope. Genuine, kind, and caring mental health providers and staff, along with family members, communicate messages that support hope for recovery. Encourage reconnection with friends and a supportive social network.

3. Build in peer support. A role model who has moved from illness to wellness in recovery inspires hope that a satisfying life is possible within the limitations encountered in living with a mental illness.

4. Encourage the individual to take control over what they can do and assist them with planning realistic goals. Listening to and encouraging the individual to share their hopes and dreams will help them embrace and commit to their recovery plan. At the same time, encourage the individual to make realistic goals that involve taking small steps.

5. Find ways to support positive attitudes and behaviors that contribute to self-esteem and well-being. Provide opportunities to practice positive self-talk and wellness behaviors (exercise, healthy eating, and stress management). Acknowledge failures and disappointments that delay reaching goals and affirm that recovery does not always follow a straight line.

As family members, we aspire to contribute to our relative's hope for a better life. At the same time, we need to find our own realistic hope to reduce frustration and disappointment resulting from unrealistic expectations. In finding realistic hope, we will be better at compassionately supporting our relative while also being compassionate toward ourselves.

MENTAL HEALTH PROFESSIONALS AS ENCOURAGERS OF HOPE

Although family members do find hope through encouragement from mental health providers and staff, some interactions in mental healthcare result in frustration, disappointment, and anger. Some frustrations are likely connected with the lack of scientific knowledge about diagnosing and treating mental illnesses. It may take years to determine an accurate diagnosis and find an effective medication and treatment plan. Although a number of challenges family members encounter in mental healthcare stem from the system's complexity and underfunding, there are actions family members can take when they are not getting information and the support they need. The following table summarizes problems and disappointments family members in my study experienced when their relative needed mental healthcare and possible actions for responding to these problems. Responding to barriers to effective care will help you and your relative find realistic hope for recovery and make your path through the mental illness maze less complicated.

ACTIONS TO ENCOURAGE HOPEFUL TREATMENT

Problem	Response
You cannot get information because your relative is over 18 and has not signed a release of information.	• When your relative is first hospitalized, ask them to sign the release of information. • You can always give information to providers and staff, although they will not be able to share information about your relative with you. • With treatment, your relative may become less irritable and be willing to sign a release of information. Keep bringing it up.
When no mental health inpatient hospital beds are immediately available, your relative is stuck in the emergency room.	Remember: safety is your relative's paramount need at this time. Although not ideal, the emergency room does provide a safe environment.

Hospital staff communicate an uncaring attitude or seem to lack compassion in interactions with your relative (lack of eye contact, not paying attention, ignoring requests).	Speak up about what you believe your relative needs.
Your relative does not accurately communicate symptoms and/or needs to mental healthcare providers and staff (e.g., "I am fine.")	Make a list of your relative's symptoms and behavior in writing and give it to the psychiatrist or relevant staff member. If you are able, go with your relative to meetings with mental health providers or staff and gently remind your relative of behaviors you have noticed.
There are no openings in transition programs after discharge from hospital.	Ask about temporary crisis housing, which provides housing and support for a week or less. If you offer to have your relative stay with you temporarily, the wait for transition treatment may be longer. Think about whether having your relative live with you would be a healthy decision for you or your relative.

There is a long wait for a psychiatrist appointment.	Consider other categories of mental health experts, such as psychiatric nurse practitioners and social workers, who would be able to consult with a psychiatrist about medications. Walk-in mental health counseling is also an option.
You are confused about how the mental healthcare system works, including terminology.	Embark on an educational journey. Ask questions, join a class for families or a support group, or search for other credible sources of information online, such as government websites and mental health organizations.

Family members also shared stories about how they admired and appreciated the competence and support of mental health providers, staff, and police officers. They were especially grateful when the psychiatrist, therapist, or mental health team provided care that met the unique needs of their relative. Family members gave examples of how providers and staff listened compassionately, confronted a relative's concerning actions, used a straightforward approach, and gave clear information to aid decision-making about needed treatment. They expressed gratitude for times when providers and staff included them in conversations and recognized the contributions family members make to treatment decisions and the recovery process. With these actions, mental health professionals assisted their journey through the mental illness maze.

The stories family members shared about their experiences with mental healthcare identify ways providers and staff can encourage hope when family members are overwhelmed. If you are a mental health professional, the following actions will communicate caring and understanding and generate hope for family members, especially helpful during a time of crisis and confusion.

- Explain privacy of health information rules (HIPAA) and provide opportunities for patients to sign a release of information. This will help communicate understanding about the family member's need to know what is happening with their relative.
- Provide information about support groups available at the hospital and through mental health organizations.
- Listen to what family members say about their relative—for example, their symptoms, unique interests, social network, and any past episodes of mental illness. In a hospital setting, reassure family members that their relative is in a safe environment.
- Explain what family members can do based on their loved one's current status. For example, if their relative is having psychotic symptoms, encourage short visits or delaying visits until symptoms have moderated.
- Encourage family members to take care of themselves and find ways to lessen the stress resulting from the current crisis.
- Carefully explain the treatment plan and what to expect from medications and other treatments, such as electroconvulsive therapy.
- Provide information about who is best to contact for information about their relative's status, treatment, and discharge plans.

- Recognize that when a family member is in the early stages of shock and denial about their relative's mental illness, unrealistic hope may help them to manage overwhelming emotions in the short term.
- Consider integration of interventions that encourage hope. Keep in mind that using the word "hope" or telling a family member "there is hope" may be deflating in the context of the adversity they have lived through in their attempts to help their relative.
- Remember that family members are a vital part of the team for supporting recovery. Using a respectful, caring approach to attend to information they contribute as well as information they need will communicate hope to family members and reassure them that their relative is getting competent care.

HOPE AND RECOVERY

Hope is essential to recovery. Remember to make your hope realistic in order to effectively encourage and support your relative's recovery journey. Think about how your hopes for your relative have changed throughout their illness. Certainly, hope for a better future can lead to actions that help achieve a future goal. You also need to keep in mind that "shattered dreams" may be the outcome of unrealistic hope.

This chapter started with the story of Anita's struggle with the idea of finding hope in a situation that seemed hopeless. When we met for a second interview, she described finding hope as she learned about supportive resources available for her youngest daughter: a mental health case manager, nurse monitoring of medications, applying for disability financial support, and a nutrition program. For Anita, mental healthcare resources are restoring her hope for effective treatment for her daughter as well as hope for respite from the constant need to respond to her daughters' mental health crises.

KEY CHAPTER MESSAGES

1. Hope helps us look forward to a better future but may result in disappointment if what is hoped for does not happen.

2. Over time, family members discovered they needed to alter their hope to look at possibilities rather than expectations.

3. Hope involves both the consideration of future possibilities and the potential consequences of these possibilities.

4. In order for hope to serve as a motivator, two processes are required: a) having a desire for a goal and a belief that it can be accomplished and b) identifying possible alternative strategies for reaching that goal along with "benchmarks" or measures that show progress.

5. Hope is beneficial for both psychosocial and physical health.

6. For family members, realistic hope often means letting go of the hope for a full recovery and instead finding hope for recovery based on what is possible for their relative to achieve.

7. Intervention strategies to promote hope include:
   - Collaborate on strategies for illness management.
   - Encourage positive relationships that communicate hope.
   - Build in peer support.
   - Encourage the individual to take control over what they can do and assist them with planning realistic goals.

- Find ways to support positive attitudes and behaviors that contribute to self-esteem and well-being.

8. Finding realistic hope will help us compassionately support our relative while also being compassionate toward ourselves.

9. Mental healthcare providers and staff are sources of hope for recovery in the provision of care to persons who live with a mental illness.

10. To promote hope for recovery for their relative, family members can take action to respond to problems and disappointments encountered in mental healthcare.

Chapter 10

BOOST RECOVERY

*Recovery is a process of change through
which people improve their health and wellness, live
self-directed lives, and strive to reach their full potential
(Substance Abuse and Mental Health Services Administration, 2019).*[1]

What is your definition of recovery for your relative? Keep in
mind that you and your relative may have different views of
what recovery means. Recovery is defined differently depending on
one's perspective—for example, yours, your relative's, or a mental
healthcare provider's. Whose view do you think will be most effective in promoting recovery? Think about which of the following
approaches would be the most helpful as well as the most realistic.

- *Service-based recovery:* Criteria for recovery include remission of symptoms, involvement in work or school, the ability

to live independently, and participation in activities with friends.

- *User-based recovery:* Criteria for recovery include being able to choose direction in one's life, establish a positive identity in the context of hopefulness, and live a satisfying life within the limitations resulting from mental illness.[2,3]

The user-based definition takes into account the viewpoint of the person who lives with a mental illness and what they need to find meaning and purpose in life. This means recovery is unique to each person and the pathway to recovery will vary. As family members, we need to support what recovery means for our relative.

This chapter explains the recovery process, summarizes research on how family members can contribute to recovery for their relatives and themselves, suggests interventions to promote recovery, and describes four study participants' stories of recovery.

UNDERSTANDING THE RECOVERY PROCESS

The acronym CHIME outlines five important components of recovery for individuals living with a mental illness.[4,5,6]

- *C*onnectedness is the process of finding satisfying relationships, receiving peer support, and becoming part of a community.
- *H*ope and optimism promote recovery by encouraging motivation and positive thinking about the future.
- *I*dentity is the development of a positive sense of self.

- *M*eaning in life includes making sense of illness experiences, having goals, and experiencing valued social roles.
- *E*mpowerment involves taking on responsibility and focusing on strengths.

In addition, consider how culture influences recovery.[5] For example, recovery that includes some level of independence is typically valued in Western cultures, while for other cultures, interdependence in family relationships may be the predominant value.[7] In this case, achieving independence may not be a desired component of recovery. Another factor to consider is how past experiences of trauma may impact the recovery process. Many people diagnosed with a serious mental illness experience traumatic events such as forced hospitalization, homelessness, abuse, or accidents. They may have trauma-related symptoms like flashbacks, nightmares, and sleep disturbances that need to be addressed in their recovery process.

RECOVERY FOR FAMILY MEMBERS

The CHIME acronym is also useful for understanding how family members recover from the stressors and emotions they experience as a result of a relative's mental illness.

Connectedness

Recovery for family members is enhanced through relationships with others who have had similar experiences. Peer support is available through support groups and family education classes.

Hope and Optimism

In addition to wanting to see their relative find hope and optimism, family members also need to maintain hope for achieving their own goals in life.

Identity

Although family members may find themselves in a caregiving role, recovery means realizing that caregiving is only one part of their life. Additionally, family members may need to overcome their own feelings of guilt and shame in the process of recovery.

Meaning in Life

An important part of the recovery process is learning how to balance limitations imposed by caregiving responsibilities with pursuing one's own life goals. Family members find meaning in getting back to their usual roles and activities and making contributions to their social network and community.

Empowerment

Family members regain control over their lives after coming through an overwhelming time of feeling little control over what happens to them. They learn to manage stress and take action to change a difficult situation.

Other Factors

The experience of trauma or secondary trauma also influences recovery for family members. Trauma may result from a relative's symptoms—such as a suicide attempt, angry outbursts, or threatening behavior—or from extreme worry about their safety. Secondary trauma may occur when a family member listens to others speak about their trauma experience or reads about a traumatic event. For example, a report on the events leading to the decision to proceed with a relative's civil commitment due to potential harm to self or others may be perceived as traumatic. In addition, family members may experience stigma and isolation related to mental illness in their family.

HOW FAMILY MEMBERS PROMOTE RECOVERY

For a person living with a mental illness, the presence and active involvement of family members contribute to a sense of belonging and experiencing emotional and practical support.[8] Canadian researchers found that families facilitated relatives' recovery by providing moral and practical support and motivating them to engage in activities that supported recovery.[9] Family members became a barrier to recovery when their interactions increased their relative's stress, they conveyed stigma or a lack of understanding for the relative's experience, or they forced hospitalization. Both criticism and overinvolvement increased relatives' stress.

In another study, family member participation in educational offerings on the recovery process led to hopefulness about the future for themselves and their relative and increased confidence in their caregiving abilities.[10] Learning about the recovery process helped family members become "recovery mentors" in supporting their relative's independence. However, when professionals predicted a poor outcome for their relative, such as continued impairment, caregivers became overwhelmed; a negative prognosis became a barrier to the relative's recovery.

In a study that explored the recovery processes of family members with a relative living with a serious mental illness, over time family members revised their ideas about what it meant to live a "normal" life.[11] They needed to confront the ambiguity of what was happening as they watched, waited, and experienced the unpredictability of their relative's behavior. They became consumed by wanting to help their relative and then experienced frustration and helplessness in interactions with the mental healthcare system. Ultimately, family members regained control of their lives by managing grief over the loss of relationships that existed prior to their relative's illness and seeking to determine who was responsible for managing the illness. Often, they alternated between calm and crises. After coping with overwhelming emotions and grief, they "adopted a stance of possibilities and realities," which led to finding hope, resolving questions of responsibility, redefining their relationships, and maintaining stability while striving for growth. Their new definition of normalcy included the desire for happiness for their relative.

INTERVENTIONS TO PROMOTE RECOVERY

Positive psychology, an approach that identifies effective interventions to promote recovery, is consistent with a user-based definition of recovery. It "seeks to understand what makes life worth living and encourages the use of mental strengths that reside in every human to confront challenges and create meaningful life experiences."[12] This approach emphasizes focusing on positive emotions and inner strengths rather than getting stuck on negative emotions. Interventions consistent with positive psychology include an assessment of strengths, gratitude and forgiveness exercises, planning satisfying activities, and replaying positive experiences by writing down three good things that happened today or this week.

Other common psychotherapy interventions used by therapists to promote recovery are cognitive behavioral therapy (CBT) and dialectical behavior therapy (DBT). The goal of CBT is to change thinking patterns, which then lead to positive behavior changes. Through CBT, individuals learn to evaluate how their thinking contributes to problems and use problem-solving skills to manage difficult situations.[13] DBT is more specifically targeted to learning how to manage emotions and reduce conflict in relationships.[14]

It is essential to involve the person who lives with a mental illness in their recovery plan. When promoting realistic goal setting for your relative, consider the following guidelines:[15]

- Personal goals must be your relative's choice. They should not be about meeting your needs or a health provider's goals.
- Choose the right level of challenge for the goal.
- Short-term goals are easier to envision in comparison to long-germ goals. Short-term goals help an individual take steps toward the long-term goal and are more likely to motivate taking action, since they seem more achievable.
- Find ways to provide immediate and meaningful feedback on progress toward meeting goals.

The beginning of this chapter defined recovery as "a process of change through which people improve their health and wellness, live self-directed lives, and strive to reach their full potential."[1] Note that this definition does not focus on the elimination of symptoms; rather, recovery is about living a satisfying and self-directed life within the limitations of symptoms. The National Alliance on Mental Illness (NAMI) emphasizes four life dimensions that support the recovery process: [1,16]

1. *Health*: the ability to make informed and healthy choices for health and well-being

2. *Home*: having a stable and safe place to live

3. *Purpose*: involvement in meaningful daily activities

4. *Community*: having relationships and social connections that contribute to a sense of friendship, love, and hope

Keep in mind that recovery may be interrupted by relapses in symptoms that could result in a crisis. It is important to be alert to potential warning signs and act to connect your relative with their mental healthcare provider early in order to prevent worsening of symptoms. Examples of concerning symptoms include feeling more tense or nervous, displaying a change in activity (either increased or decreased), and having greater difficulty sleeping and concentrating.[17] Although relapses may occur, a recovery plan can assist your relative in getting back on track once again and may help to avoid hospitalization.

Recovery Resources

Structured recovery programs offer opportunities for persons living with a mental illness to engage in making a recovery plan.

NAMI's Family-to-Family Class curriculum identifies the following examples of effective recovery programs:[18]

- The Wellness Recovery Action Plan (WRAP) is a self-designed recovery program that facilitates the use of wellness tools and daily activities to stay well, identifies early warning signs of an impending crisis and how to respond to the signs, and provides the opportunity to create a crisis and post-crisis plan. (**www.mentalhealthrecovery.com**)

- Whole Health Action Management (WHAM) offers strategies and peer support to increase resiliency, wellness, and self-management by focusing on building the habit of healthy behavior. Strategies include developing strengths, creating a weekly action plan, participating in peer support groups, managing stress, reframing negative thinking, and using a shared decision-making form for meetings with healthcare providers. This program is offered by the Center of Excellence for Integrated Health Solutions through the Substance Abuse and Mental Health Services Administration. (**https://www.center-4healthandsdc.org/uploads/7/1/1/4/71142589/wham_participant_guide.pdf**)

- NAMI Peer-to-Peer is an eight-week education program focused on improving communication skills, strengthening relationships, and setting goals for the future. (**https://www.nami.org/Support-Education/Mental-Health-Education/NAMI-Peer-to-Peer**)

The Meaning of Recovery for Our Relative

Remember that recovery belongs to our relative, so it makes sense to work on understanding what they are experiencing. Our relative may be dealing with feelings of failure, guilt, and despair ensuing from the impact of symptoms on their life. Trying to change the situation may seem daunting or impossible. They may need to face unrealistic expectations for recovery and work through accepting a new reality for their life. Although we are likely to be impatient with a relative's long recovery process, we must remember to give them their autonomy to make choices. You can help by keeping things simple, since focusing on one change at a time may be what they can do. If your relative is living with you, it is important to establish clear rules regarding their actions in your home as part of your own self-care. Be sensitive to the space they need—rest is essential to recovery after symptoms have diminished one's ability to function day to day.

Key Messages to Share with Your Relative

The NAMI Family-to-Family class curriculum includes reading a letter written by an author who lives with a mental illness.[19] In it, the writer asks family members to understand their experience and notes three things their family member can do for them: 1) learn about their illness, 2) help them find effective treatment, and 3) listen with an open heart and mind. Although your relative's illness likely added difficulty to your life, understanding mental illness as a disease will help you put the difficulties in perspective. Know that finding effective treatment often takes time and persistence. You can be an advocate for your relative in helping them give voice to their needs. Listening works better than giving advice. Your relative needs time to develop confidence to take steps toward recovery—episodes of mental illness often leave one exhausted and overwhelmed. You can be a sounding board and affirm good decisions made by your relative as they move toward recovery.

STORIES OF RECOVERY

For the participants in my study, their own recovery processes often occurred in tandem with their relative's. The following recovery stories of four family members illustrate how they experienced recovery for their relative and for themselves. Consider how the CHIME components (connectedness, hope and optimism, identity, meaning in life, and empowerment) occur in these stories.

Sharon's Story

Sharon's adult daughter, Gabrielle, exhibited anxiety and angry outbursts in childhood; in college, she was diagnosed with bipolar disorder. Although Sharon had extensive knowledge about mental health from her role as a public health educator, she was shaken when faced with Gabrielle's first hospitalization during her first year of college. Soon after Gabrielle's diagnosis, Sharon experienced the crisis of having to call the police when her daughter threatened to injure herself.

Sharon promoted connectedness for Gabrielle by encouraging her to find a meaningful work situation and develop healthy friendships. She built her own connectedness through joining a class for family members and becoming friends with two mothers who also have adult daughters living with a mental illness.

Her approach to interacting with Gabrielle is predominantly hopeful and optimistic; she sees herself as "calm and uplifting" in conversations with her daughter. She tries to create environments where Gabrielle will thrive and recounted how she gave her daughter the opportunity to redesign her room after moving back home following hospitalization. Sharon sees herself as a generally optimistic person: "I count my blessings. I really live a life of gratitude."

As a mother of a young adult, Sharon recognizes it is important for Gabrielle to establish her independent identity. When healthcare providers needed information about Gabrielle's symptoms, Sharon explained, "I don't speak on her behalf and belittle her." She separates Gabrielle's symptoms from who she is as a person. Sharon finds she needs to balance supporting her daughter's autonomy and respecting her young adult status with helping her navigate the mental healthcare system.

Gabrielle and Sharon both found meaning in life when they presented a breakout session at a NAMI conference together. Gabrielle is proud of her advocacy role; she posts mental health events and information on Facebook. Both mother and daughter have found meaning in Gabrielle's illness experience. Sharon's experience with her daughter has inspired her goal to reduce the stigma often associated with mental illness and stop the silence by promoting the "make it okay" message, which conveys that it is acceptable to talk about mental illness.

Sharon empowers Gabrielle by coaching her on taking responsibility for managing finances; she focuses on her daughter's strengths. Gabrielle now lives in her own apartment, has a job, and is becoming increasingly self-sufficient in her recovery. Sharon also recognizes her own strengths and is empowered to make decisions that contribute to her well-being, such as getting adequate sleep and choosing healthy friendships.

Also, Sharon knows that recovery is a process, and she is realistic about possible setbacks. She questioned Gabrielle's ability to be independent and wondered if her own burden would be never-ending. Would she need to take care of her daughter for the rest of her life? As family members, we hold these tensions in tandem, tempering hope and optimism with realism about how situations can change. Yet, we have gratitude for the good times.

Jim's Story

Ten years ago, Jim's wife, Monica, experienced shifting moods, frequently called in sick to work, lost her job as a teacher, and attempted suicide. Jim stayed by her side through several hospitalizations and failed medications. Finally, electroconvulsive therapy (ECT) alleviated Monica's symptoms. Jim persevered through doubts about his ability to manage the challenges his wife's symptoms brought to their relationship.

> *There's been plenty of times when I thought could I do better. There were a number of times where I wanted to just get up and leave—call it quits. I started thinking, "I don't deserve this," or, "What did I do to deserve this?"*

Both Monica and Jim modified their life patterns to build a meaningful life within the limitations stemming from Monica's symptoms of mental illness.

Jim promotes connectedness for Monica by recognizing the importance of her participation in church activities and a support group as part of her recovery plan. However, Jim found support groups were not helpful for him. He commented, "I started hearing other people's stories and it's like I really don't belong here." Each person needs to find their own way of connecting. For Jim, work relationships are satisfying, and he finds reward in projects such as yardwork that take his mind off family concerns. He also noted that he, Monica, and his young adult son have become closer through helping Monica work toward recovery.

Monica and Jim have hope for continued stability in her recovery. She is currently looking for part-time work. Although financial challenges mean the couple need to watch their budget, they envision a future of finding satisfaction in a simpler life. They overcame threatened foreclosure on their home and learned to make do with older appliances.

In an example of promoting positive identity, Jim encouraged Monica to take over management of the couple's finances after her recent short-term work experience at a bank. Although Monica had previously engaged in extreme online shopping, Jim trusted her to keep track of their budget, and she did so successfully. While acknowledging the losses in their lives, Jim's identity became one of taking on responsibility and keeping the family together. He balanced work and childcare responsibilities when Monica was first hospitalized. Later, as he responded to Monica's need for support and his son's episode of depression, Jim saw himself as being "the rock" of the family and took control to cope with family challenges.

Both Jim and Monica found meaning in life after they gave up drinking. After Monica's DUI, Jim realized their habit of going out drinking at night was contributing to her difficulties. He stopped supporting her drinking habit by refusing to go with her to bars.

They now both find meaning in daily activities that are satisfying to them. Jim finds meaning in organizing his time around Monica's schedule, which promotes her recovery.

Jim's actions in his relationship with Monica have contributed to a sense of empowerment in her recovery. Examples include empowering her to take over management of family finances and encouraging her to do things she likes, such as working with crafts and attending church-related activities. Jim experiences empowerment through effectively dealing with financial challenges, being a dependable source of support for his family, and consistently considering the experiences and viewpoints of his wife and son in the choices he makes.

Dick's Story

Dick took on primary caregiving responsibilities for his brother, Stuart, after their mother was no longer able to oversee his mental healthcare. Stuart was first hospitalized at age 19 and then had difficulty finding effective treatment until ECT decreased his troublesome symptoms. Following a long period of stability, stress related to his real estate business triggered the escalation of his manic symptoms and a series of hospitalizations. Currently, Stuart is managing his symptoms with medication, is financially independent, and lives on his own in a cabin several hours away from Dick.

Dick encourages Stuart, who recently retired, to stay engaged in the community by getting out of his cabin to do activities he enjoys. However, Stuart's sedentary lifestyle due to a leg amputation after a motorcycle accident and weight gain related to his psychiatric medications have limited his ability to leave home and connect with others. Dick suggested he get back to a favorite activity, fishing, but

Stuart tells him that no one will go fishing with him; Dick believes Stuart will not ask anyone to go with him.

As a co-teacher of a NAMI Family-to-Family class, Dick has found valued community connections. He is also connected with friends and lives with his partner. They care for her four-year-old grandson, which he said gives him "joy."

Hope and optimism are difficult for Dick to find in the recovery process. Although he is saddened and frustrated by Stuart's lifestyle and the inadequacies of the mental healthcare system in helping Stuart, he also contemplated the possibility of his brother's hope for life beyond current miseries.

> *Morbidly obese. Sedentary. Chain-smoker. Takes a fistful of pills, morning and night. I'm somewhat fatalistic. You have a guilty thought. If he passed away, he's out of his misery. I am not religious. My brother doesn't show any outward signs of being religious. He doesn't go to church. He doesn't talk about spirituality or God or anything. But I think he believes he's going to heaven. I believe he thinks that.*

Dick finds hope in teaching family members about mental illness and strategies for coping.

In the past, Dick promoted a positive identity for Stuart by helping him with his real estate business. Stuart owned the business and supervised a small group of employees. Dick saw him several times a week to help keep the business going and requested feedback from the employees about any manic symptoms they observed in Stuart's behavior. Although often ambivalent about taking on primary caregiving responsibilities for his brother, Dick does live out an advocacy role in helping his brother get what he needs in his recovery journey.

Dick has found meaning in life through staying involved with his brother's mental healthcare. He goes to appointments with Stuart and brings a list of symptoms to share with the psychiatrist, since Stuart may not mention them. One time, when mental healthcare providers were concerned about Stuart failing to take all his medications, they suggested he should use a pillbox. Stuart didn't want a pillbox, but Dick convinced him to use one. Though he has taken on the caregiving responsibility, Dick chooses to avoid dwelling on his brother's situation and views his home by a lake as a refuge. He seeks out life experiences and roles that give him respite from a constant focus on his brother's problems.

Although he doesn't always agree with Stuart's choices, Dick empowers him by respecting his autonomy, with the caveat that he lives in a safe situation. For example, Dick suggested that ECT might be a better choice for treatment in contrast to the side effects resulting from psychiatric medications. At this point, Stuart is resisting ECT, which Dick accepts as long as Stuart doesn't need hospitalization. Dick experiences empowerment through learning strategies for responding to mental illness symptoms. In the past, he tried to logically argue with Stuart when he expressed unrealistic thoughts or ideas. Now, he uses the LEAP (Listen-Empathize-Agree-Partner) method described by Xavier Amador in his book *I Am Not Sick I Don't Need Help*, which he has found to be an effective guide for interacting with his brother.

Dick continues to struggle with whether he is doing the right thing for his brother. Since Stuart has moved farther away, he is ambivalent about visiting and sees him less often.

I don't interact with him as often. My life is certainly better not interacting with him all the time. But am I doing the right thing by stepping away? That guilt piece again. You tell yourself you can only do what you can do. Since he's changed his medication, I've been obviously trying to be more involved. I tell myself I need to go up there and spend a day every week. I haven't done it because I don't want to.

Dick and Stuart's experiences illustrate the changing nature of recovery processes. Our relatives may experience setbacks, and we may experience ambivalence about our own recovery and our effectiveness in managing the unpredictability and uncertainty of supporting a relative living with a mental illness.

Jessica's Story

When Jessica was a teenager, she came home one day to find her mother, Diane, acting erratically. Jessica called her dad, who was out of town for work, to come help. Once Diane was back on medications and had structure in her life, she successfully fulfilled her roles as a mother, wife, and employee.

Jessica's family values relationships. Early on, Diane sought family therapy as well as individual therapy for Jessica. Diane loves being a grandmother and spends more time with her grandchildren now that she is retired. Jessica always makes sure her mother has time with her school-age kids, and along with her sister, connects with Diane through family activities. The sisters also provide some financial support for their mother following her retirement.

Hope and optimism are predominant in Jessica's relationship with her mother. She describes Diane as funny, jovial, active, and caring. Their family uses humor to cope with difficult situations. Jessica hopes her mother will continue to live a well-balanced life into old age.

When Diane expresses doubts about herself, Jessica promotes a positive identity for her mother. She affirms Diane's involvement in their family life by explaining to her children how their grandma comes to help. Jessica's life choices contribute to her own positive identity. She spoke about how she has learned to effectively manage stress. When she was home alone with two young children while her husband served in the military, she felt overwhelmed by sadness and anxiety. Her mother noticed her sadness and suggested she see a mental health professional. Jessica followed through with her mother's suggestion, continues to be observant about her responses to life challenges, and seeks help when needed to manage stress.

Diane finds meaning in life through her family relationships and the contributions she makes to her daughters' families. Jessica believes that her experiences with her mother contributed to her effectiveness in teaching clients about ways to be healthy in her role as a public health educator. She encourages people with disabilities to confront obstacles that interfere with learning. She is wary about putting labels on others, because she knows there are so many variations in individuals' personalities. She checks in with her clients and family members in order to pay attention to what is going in their life and aims to address their anxiety, stress, or concerns by talking with them to provide relief and show support.

Both Diane and Jessica illustrate living empowered lives—they have taken responsibility in their life roles and look for what they can contribute to one another's well-being. Although Jessica acknowledges life with her mother is not always easy, she sees good things coming out of her experience. She has learned it is possible to "live a normal life when faced with adversity." As a result, she has an increased capacity for empathy for others.

RECOVERY IS NOT "ONE SIZE FITS ALL"

Each relative in the previous four stories experienced a different trajectory and timeline for their recovery processes. You can use your knowledge of recovery processes and a hopeful attitude to help your relative understand that you want them to make life choices that are satisfying. That means letting go of your ideas about what you think your relative needs to do.

You have more control over your own recovery. Family members in my study promoted their recovery by connecting with others who had similar experiences, especially through classes and support groups. While a few family members did stop hoping for recovery for their relatives because of many relapses and perceived risk of behavior that could lead to harm for the family members, they all had hope for their own recovery and their ability to get through difficult times with intact self-esteem and a positive identity. Many family members found meaning in life by advocating for their relative and others who live with a mental illness. They were empowered to take control over their responses to situations, engage in self-care, and make choices to strengthen their well-being and ease their journey through the mental illness maze.

KEY CHAPTER MESSAGES

1. In recovery, people make life choices to help them move toward well-being and a satisfying life within the limitations resulting from their illness.

2. Recovery may be defined as service-based or user-based. Criteria for service-based recovery include remission of symptoms, involvement in work or school, the ability to live independently, and participation in activities with friends. Criteria for user-based recovery include being able to take control of one's life, establish a positive identity in the context of hopefulness, and live a satisfying life within the limitations resulting from mental illness.

3. Family members also experience recovery processes as they cope with difficulties brought about by a relative's mental illness.

4. The CHIME acronym describes components of recovery: connectedness, hope and optimism, identity, meaning in life, and empowerment.

5. In addition to the CHIME recovery components, two factors that may influence recovery are cultural background and the experience of trauma.

6. To facilitate a relative's recovery, provide moral and practical support, offer affirmation that leads to a sense of belonging, and stay actively involved in your relative's life.

7. Family members hindered recovery when they increased their relative's stress, conveyed stigma, contributed to forcing hospitalization, became overinvolved, or criticized their relative.

8. Be deliberate about choosing interventions to support recovery.
   - Use positive psychology, which emphasizes focusing on positive emotions and inner strengths rather than getting stuck on negative emotions.
   - Always remember that the recovery plan belongs to your relative—not to you or their healthcare provider.
   - Encourage realistic goal setting—goals should be the right level of challenge and short-term. Provide feedback along their recovery journey.
   - Keep in mind that relapses may occur. A recovery plan will help your relative get back on track and may help them avoid hospitalizations.
   - Consider suggesting structured recovery programs for your relative, such as WRAP, WHAM, and NAMI Peer-to-Peer.

9. Above all, keep your relative's meaning of recovery in mind as you interact with them.

Chapter 11

FOLLOW A SELF-CARE RECIPE

Five ingredients for a happy, better life are "sleeping well,
eating well, exercising, socializing, and not stressing out"
(Heather, study participant).

"**S**elf-care is any activity that we do deliberately in order to take care of our mental, emotional, and physical health."[1] As you engage in self-care, you are building the resilience, motivation, and strength needed to support your relative during times of symptom escalation and crisis.

At the end of the final class, participants in one of my National Alliance on Mental Illness (NAMI) family classes explained what they learned: 1) they acquired more compassion toward their relative, and 2) they embraced self-care. Clearly, these two themes are connected. Effective self-care strategies empower family members to feel more compassion for their relative's experience with mental illness.

Over time, stress and burden from caregiving responsibilities often lead to worse emotional and physical health. Your well-being may be negatively affected by an ongoing stress response with little respite; continuing anxiety and worry; inadequate sleep; and poor habits such as a lack of exercise, unhealthy eating, or substance use. When you believe that your stress is bad and you cannot change or manage it, your physical and mental health will likely worsen. Self-care strategies will help increase your ability to cope well with stressful events and situations. By engaging in healthy self-care strategies, you will be more likely to find reward and satisfaction in your caregiving activities.

This chapter highlights helpful self-care strategies used by four family members in my study and discusses key guidelines and ideas for effective self-care. Family members coped in very different ways but found joy and satisfaction in taking time for themselves. They became calmer, more peaceful, and more effective in interactions with their ill relative. Self-care strategies assisted them in finding their way through the mental illness maze.

WHAT SELF-CARE STRATEGIES WERE MOST HELPFUL?

The self-care strategies that worked for family members in my study varied greatly. Some family members extolled the benefits of support groups, while others found they were uncomfortable in support groups. Although many found it helpful to talk to their friends about difficult situations regarding an ill relative, others were worried about losing friendships and deliberately did not share their concerns with friends. Some family members discovered that others in their family, particularly extended family, added to stress when they did not understand their relative's mental illness or made unhelpful suggestions. For others, spouses/partners and siblings provided stress relief when they listened and shared care responsibilities. Many family members deliberately focused on their wellness through exercise and healthy eating and by getting adequate sleep. The following stories illustrate what is possible in the realm of self-care.

Anita: Art and Hockey

Anita finds that creating art helps her release emotions resulting from the challenges she encounters in caring for her two daughters, who both live with a mental illness. In the summer after her older daughter Serena's first hospitalization for a manic episode, Anita worked on an art exhibition with a mental illness theme; she visualized her emotions through her art. During this time, symptoms exhibited by Nina, her younger daughter, led to confusion and concern. Anita described how she used eggs as an art form to communicate her reeling emotions.

> *I made mostly eggs because the whole thing of mental illness felt fragile to me. It was like this need to encase, enclose, protect not only them, but our family, that whole experience. Also not knowing what this is—like the mystery of an egg. What's going to happen and the hope you have for an egg and how that changes. One piece I made was an egg with a hole through it, and that to me represented a punch in the gut. I experienced confusion, frustration, and anger over what appeared to be Nina's deceit and lack of follow-through. Oh my God. What's going on? When*

I understood more, it was this window. The hole was like this window that led to compassion versus anger. I also did another egg of me with my mouth wide open screaming because of this anger [I had] until I understood. Because she seemed so functional, I felt like she was just messing with us. She wouldn't open up and we couldn't understand.

As another self-care strategy, Anita focuses on her strengths and advantages in life.

I'm really strong. I have had many blessings in my life. I have had so much privilege as a white person and as someone who can function well. I always had a safety net with my parents. I don't know if I ever used it. But it was always there—I knew it.

Anita invests in both physical and emotional outlets. She began playing hockey in her 40s. Hockey is a physical outlet that allows her to think about the present moment. She goes on walks with a friend who has a son living with a mental illness, and they share their parenting experiences. She attends a support group, meets with a therapist, and participates in NAMI events. As a guardian ad litem volunteer, she advocates for children's best interests in the court system.

When asked about her suggestions for other parents of children living with a mental illness, Anita declared, "Take care of yourself, physically, emotionally, socially. Learn boundaries. Teflon. I have to think of Teflon. Let things slide off. I'm not good at it, but I try." Anita used the phrase "soldiering on" to describe how she copes with challenges in her life related to her daughters' symptoms of mental illness.

Her array of self-care strategies makes it possible for her to persevere in finding effective treatment and resources for her daughters.

Brenda: Swimming and Gardening

Although Brenda experienced considerable chaos and disruption in life stemming from her husband Don's manic episodes, she persevered in encouraging him to make choices to promote his recovery. When she realized that Don was planning to return home following time in jail and the hospital, she moved out, given his anger toward her and fear for her safety. Then hospital staff contacted her with concerns about Don's ability to care for himself. Brenda returned home to monitor his symptom management. She has adapted to Don's obsessive-compulsive tendencies, now manages their family finances, and considers her husband's perspectives on what he needs in daily life. Initially, Brenda wondered whether she was contributing to Don's struggle in some way.

> Before he actually got diagnosed and before he moved out of the house I was to the point where I thought maybe there is actually something wrong with me. I was starting to double-question myself. Am I being unrealistic here? I talked to a gal at work. and she suggested the employee assistance program. I went to four counseling sessions with the program.

Brenda asked, "What in the world did I do to deserve this?" Although her first husband passed away after declining from alcoholism and drug abuse, she did not realize the potential future complications she would face in living with Don.

I didn't see this one coming at all. Living with alcoholism and drug abuse was one thing. But going into the world of mental illness was totally different. I grew up in mental illness because my mom had major depression. I never knew my mom to be well. She had always been sick and struggling with depression and anxiety and anger. But never to that level. Okay, we are in the Twilight Zone here. I was reaching out to friends and neighbors and pastors and nobody really had any answers for me.

But Brenda did persist in finding answers. She continued to reach out and found support from family, friends, work, church, NAMI, and Alcoholics Anonymous. In addition, she engages in an active lifestyle to help her deal with stress.

I go swimming at least two, three times a week. I garden. If I'm frustrated, I'm out in the garden. We don't have a lot of weeds in that garden. I've dealt with stress for years. In the winter time I work out every day at home for half an hour before I come into work.

Brenda now focuses on her strengths. She concluded, "I'm definitely a stronger person than I thought I was. I would say I'm more compassionate for people that have to live with mental illness and their families. I can be supportive to them." She has met many good people in the NAMI family support group she co-leads and finds reward in supporting others who have had experiences similar to hers. She has learned to focus on activities that give her joy.

It's so overwhelming looking at the future. I always say you got to stay in today. Count your blessings.

Get a gratitude notebook and write down every day three things you're grateful for. You can't focus on how overwhelming and how horrible life is right now. You've got to find something to hang on to. Find joy in something you do and learn to take care of yourself. That's why I do my exercises. That's why I do my gardening. Whatever you can do to take care of yourself. Because if you let yourself get run down, you can't take care of anybody else. You can't love anybody else if you don't love yourself. If they won't get help, at least get help for yourself. That's huge. Reach out to others and call if you have questions, contact NAMI. There's people out there that can help. But you have to ask for it.

Brenda tells us to let go of the past, make the best of today, and go forward.

Heather: Writing in Journals

Heather found ways to work through the emotions resulting from having both a brother and husband who live with a mental illness. Her husband, Scott, effectively manages his bipolar disorder by taking medication and maintaining structure in his life, while her brother, Brad, lives at home with his parents and has greater difficulty finding and maintaining effective treatment related to his diagnosis of schizoaffective disorder. Journal writing became one of Heather's early coping strategies, as she put events and emotions related to family mental illness on paper. She wrote about how her brother's actions negatively affected her parents, her own challenge in trying to understand mental illness, and her experiences with panic attacks.

After five years of journaling, Heather wrote thank you letters to a magazine and a historical society for their attention to mental health, resulting in publication of her letters; she described this experience as "cool" and "empowering." Through attending a NAMI Family-to-Family class, reflective journaling, and her advocacy activities, Heather now recognizes her own strengths. She believes the most important skills she has learned are listening and self-care. She sought out therapy and recently completed an interactive online program called "Beating the Blues" that helped her identify and stop negative thought patterns. She described what she has learned are the five ingredients "to this happy, better life—sleeping well, eating well, exercising, socializing, and not stressing out." She also noted, "It's hard to put yourself first. But if you don't, it makes all your other relationships and work harder." Heather summed up her approach to managing life stressors as "listening, self-care, finding a way to express yourself, and then being really gentle with yourself."

Abby: Self-Reflection

At the time of the interviews, Abby was in the midst of coping with her mother Mandy's repeated hospitalizations and unsuccessful treatment; Abby, her father, sister, and two brothers had come together to make choices about treatment options. One coping strategy Abby uses is "compartmentalizing"—for example, she decided not to worry about her mother when at work. She puts effort into maintaining relationships with friends because she sees the effect of a lack of friendships on her mother. She uses self-reflection to examine her relationships; she explained that she recognizes that some of her social behaviors stem from her experience with her mother.

> *I feel like I'm a super people pleaser and very cognizant if people feel uncomfortable. I don't confront anyone. I don't get into arguments. I just want to avoid all that stuff. That's a result of feeling that way with my mom.*

In light of this reflection, Abby is thinking about how to be more deliberate in her responses to others. She also recognizes her need for encouragement in caring for herself. She noted, "You definitely need someone to help you realize, 'I need to take care of me.' It's hard to say that to yourself. When someone else says it, you [think], 'Okay, I can see that.'" She talked about finding joy and satisfaction in caring for her young daughter and doing good work for her job.

Abby has learned about managing the many emotions emerging from her family experiences. Key lessons include the importance of self-care and coming together as a family.

> *I think the good part has been for me being able to realize how important it is to take care of yourself. My dad and I feel like all of us have to realize if you're feeling off or anything, going back to your home base and taking care of you is really important. There are both challenges and good things about coming together as a family. I think we spend more time together than we would have because of the tensions and challenges.*

Encouragement from both her husband and father motivate Abby to engage in self-care and invest time in improving her well-being. Through self-reflection, setting boundaries, and being open to receiving support, she has found a life balance that keeps her healthy while also collaborating with her family on how to promote recovery for her mother.

WHEN SELF-CARE MEANS LETTING GO

For some family members, self-care meant letting go of the commitment to constantly "be there" for their ill relative. Letting go of a futile effort to make things better or "fix" them resulted in recovering a peaceful and meaningful life without their relative. In order to let go, they needed to overcome guilt, anger, disappointment, and other emotions that are destructive in the long term. It takes courage to let go when you desire a different outcome with all your heart. If responding to your relative's symptoms is harmful to your mental or physical well-being, you may need a respite or even a long-term "letting go" of taking on responsibility for your relative's well-being. This also means letting go of guilt that may follow your decision. Take a deep breath and give yourself permission to let go!

SELF-CARE GUIDELINES

An abundance of books and websites offer self-care guidelines, strategies, and tips. Despite how impossible it may seem when you are already feeling overwhelmed and overworked, make time for self-care in your life. Above all, do not feel guilty about taking care of yourself. Explore different ideas for self-care and choose what works best for you. The family members in my study demonstrated a vast array of self-care activities, including playing hockey, swimming, gardening, engaging in art, participating in mindfulness and meditation, and journaling. They found that volunteering gave them rewards and satisfaction. The majority of study participants sought out classes and support groups, which gave them a sense of control over their own knowledge about mental illness and how they respond to their relative. The family members made new connections and asked for help.

Barriers to Self-Care

You may need to overcome barriers that get in the way of implementing self-care strategies. One of these barriers is the feeling that you are being selfish. Know that paying attention to yourself does not mean you are a narcissist. Rather, it is about being mindful of what you need to do to stay healthy and confident so you can fulfill your roles and responsibilities.[2] Self-care is about loving both yourself and others.

Another barrier to self-care is believing we do not have time for it. We put ourselves last and may feel guilty if we prioritize "time for me."[3] To counter this barrier, schedule self-care into your day. That way, it becomes a "must-happen" rather than a "nice-to-happen" event.

NAMI Guidelines for Taking Care of Yourself

Of the many available guidelines on self-care, NAMI offers strategies targeted specifically to family members who have a relative living with a mental illness.[4]

Understand how stress affects you.

We all experience stress differently. Do you have physical symptoms such as headaches, stomach problems, body aches, or trouble sleeping? Do you have excess anxiety? Do you resort to unhealthy habits such as excess eating, shopping, television watching, or alcohol use? Note your responses to stress and determine how you can best manage overwhelming stress in your life.

Protect your physical health.

You likely know what this means—exercise daily, eat well, get enough sleep, avoid alcohol and drugs, and practice relaxation exercises.

Recharge yourself.

Make time for yourself and don't get distracted by what you think you should be doing. Time out helps you to avoid becoming consumed with caregiving responsibilities. Choose a fun activity that you enjoy.

Practice good mental habits.

This means not judging yourself for having negative emotions and avoiding getting caught in the guilt trap. Look for the positive in each day. Gather strength from others and be willing to accept help.

Additional Self-Care Wisdom

Self-care involves being mindful about the need for boundaries in your relationship with your relative. Although setting boundaries may be difficult because of fear of hurting or angering your relative, you may need to set limits in response to their actions when they are with you or in your home. Family members in my study learned to set boundaries after repeatedly experiencing negative effects on their lives from a relative's escalating symptoms. Setting limits became part of their self-care repertoire.

Build recharging activities into your day. "Self-Care 101," a list of 10 tips on the Psychology Today website, suggests finding a daily way to decompress. Refresh your brain by taking mini-breaks such as going on short walk, having a brief conversation, or looking at photos.[2] Spiritual self-care can also help you recharge. You may find spiritual inspiration through meditation, prayer, a motivational reading or video, attending a religious service, being in nature, or keeping a gratitude journal.

You can be more intentional about your self-care by developing a plan for goals and activities. The NAMI website features a Self-Care Inventory, a checklist you can use to rate how often you do physical, psychological, emotional, spiritual, and work-related self-care activities.[5] The inventory is useful for identifying specific strategies for improving self-care.

In addition, Princeton University's website offers a printable wellness self-assessment and guidance for developing a self-care plan.[6] The assessment categories address emotional, environmental, intellectual, occupational, physical, social, and spiritual wellness.

Another excellent source for guidance on wellness activities is a downloadable publication by the Substance Abuse and Mental

Health Services Administration, *Creating a Healthier Life: A Step-by-Step Guide to Wellness.*[7]

To create an effective self-care plan, make your goals SMART:[6,8]

- **S**pecific – What are the concrete details of your plan (what, where, when, why)?
- **M**easurable – How will you know you accomplished the goal?
- **A**chievable – Is your goal achievable and easy to put into action?
- **R**ealistic – What resources do you need (time, equipment, involvement of others)?
- **T**ime-bound – What time frame do you need to reach the goal?

SMART goals are used extensively in business, public health, and personal health. Taking time to craft specific goals will provide motivation and control as you move forward with your self-care plan.

Think about what is possible to control in your interactions with your relative. There is much we cannot control about our relative's experience with mental illness. We often do not know what will happen day to day and are afraid of thinking about what the future will bring. Look at what you can control today. Self-care means looking for what you can control and knowing what you cannot. Here are some examples of things you can control or change in your life.[9]

- How much you argue
- How often you smile
- Your tone of voice
- What you pay attention to
- Your point of view

- How isolated you feel
- How you deal with stress
- How much you worry
- How you spend your money
- What substances you use
- How you help
- What kind of help you get

Notice that all these examples have to do with YOU—not someone else. Taking care of you results in having more energy to attend to your family's needs. Also, taking care of you can enable someone else to benefit from your gifts and experience. Many family members in my study engaged in helping others as volunteers and in their careers because it was something they could do well and brought a sense of purpose and satisfaction to their lives.

You and other members of your family will have more calm, peaceful, and happy times if you make time for fun activities and what is important to you. Changing our life patterns can be challenging because we often revert to past routines and behaviors. It may take a while to integrate self-care into daily life. Consider starting with one or two self-care activities as you begin a self-care routine. Note how you feel before and how you feel after. Pay attention to which activities give you the most satisfaction and stress relief. Remember, self-care is about you and is up to you. What is your recipe for self-care?

CREATE A SELF-CARE CHECKLIST

You can jump-start your self-care plan by creating a checklist. There are many examples of self-care checklists available online, or you can make your own. Brainstorm activities for specific categories of self-care (physical, social, emotional, mental, and spiritual). Here are a few suggestions:

Category	Activity
Physical	• Walk outside for 30 minutes. • Make a nutritious meal that includes fruits and vegetables.
Social	• Connect with a friend on the phone or in person. • Join a class or book club.
Emotional	• Accept support from others. • Engage in positive self-talk.
Mental	• Take a break each day. • Learn something new.
Spiritual	• Volunteer for an organization. • Spend time reflecting in nature.

Identify three to five items for each category that capture your self-care goals and make them specific to what is important to you. Also, plan a time to periodically review your checklist, whether daily or weekly. Ready, set, go!

KEY CHAPTER MESSAGES

1. Self-care involves intentional, self-directed actions that contribute positively to physical, mental, and emotional well-being.

2. Self-care is an important coping strategy for managing the stress and burden resulting from a relative's mental health crises and symptoms.

3. When you engage in self-care activities, you are more likely to experience satisfaction with your caregiving activities.

4. For family members who have long-term experiences in trying to help a relative who lives with a serious mental illness, self-care may sometimes mean letting go of caregiving responsibilities.

5. Barriers to engaging in self-care include feeling that you are being selfish and that you don't have time to do things for yourself.

6. NAMI's self-care guidelines are:
   • Understand how stress affects you.
   • Protect your physical health.
   • Recharge yourself.
   • Practice good mental habits.

7. Maintaining personal boundaries and setting limits for relatives is an important component of self-care.

8. Developing a self-care plan with specific goals for improving your well-being will motivate you to improve your self-care.

9. Improving your self-care is something you can control when other aspects of your life feel out of control.

Chapter 12

SPEAK UP ABOUT MENTAL HEALTH

Advocacy means that we speak and act on behalf of ourselves or others. Mental health advocacy involves giving voice to the needs and concerns of vulnerable individuals who live with a mental illness.

Although mental health advocacy may seem like a daunting undertaking, advocacy actions do increase awareness about the needs of people living with a mental illness and affect decision-making that improves access to mental healthcare. As advocates, we give a voice to those who are unable to ask for or get the help they need, whether because they are unwilling or do not know how. Advocacy promotes the autonomy of people living with a mental illness. It also reduces discrimination, which results when the perspectives of people who live with a mental illness are not heard or understood. The following situations in systems of care lead to discrimination for persons who live with a mental illness:[1]

- Insufficient attention is given to an individual's mental health history.
- Treatment is based on an established standard, with little attention given to individual uniqueness.
- The diagnosis conveys an expectation for outcomes.
- Individuals are not informed about treatment options or included in decision-making.
- Available mental health resources are low quality and not based on evidence.

When someone lives with a mental illness, we can use advocacy actions to call attention to their experience in order to influence decisions that affect them.[2,3] The family members I interviewed for my study all advocated for effective treatment and services for their relative. After dealing with mental health crises and learning new coping strategies, many also engaged in community advocacy activities. This chapter provides examples of how family members advocated for relatives and for improved mental health services, discusses the characteristics of advocacy, suggests strategies for advocating for oneself and others, and outlines a framework for systems-level advocacy.

STORIES OF ADVOCACY

When family members advocated for effective treatment for their relative, their actions often resulted in better care. When possible, they participated in the hospital admission process and attended therapy or psychiatrist appointments with their relative to better explain their observations of symptoms and advocate for treatment fine-tuned to address their relative's symptoms.

Advocating for a Loved One

Sharon, whose young adult daughter, Gabrielle, lives with bipolar disorder, spoke about being a "fierce advocate" for her daughter in interactions with the mental healthcare system. She explained, "I'm a fierce advocate in terms of the continuum of care and accessing care. I have no problem being a fierce mom [and] getting my kid what she needs." As a public health educator on mental health topics, she views herself as an "ambassador" who loves someone who lives with a mental illness. She does not use the word "suffering" when describing individuals who live with a mental illness; Sharon focuses on the person first. She states, "My daughter, Gabrielle, lives with bipolar." Sharon's advocacy reduces the stigma often associated with mental illness.

Connie persisted in finding mental health services that met her daughter Naomi's needs for diversity in her treatment team. She also obtained consent for release of information so she could be more actively involved in decisions about Naomi's treatment choices. Advocacy is an important component of Connie's new skill set in helping her daughter navigate the mental healthcare system.

> *Having the word "advocacy"—to advocate for someone. Just knowing that [I can advocate] helped. Because I'm not being the bitchy mom. I'm not being the controlling parent. It's like, no, I'm advocating for what's in the best interest of my child.*

Connie does not hesitate to talk to others about mental illness. She explained to her current employer that she would choose her daughter over her job. In addition, she contributed to developing a program for first responders to address mental health crises in her work setting.

Katie felt great responsibility for finding treatment for her brother, Kevin, whose life was derailed by a serious mental illness.

> *There were many times where I brought him to the psych ward and would update the whole family. I talked to doctors about meds and made sure he was on the 72-hour hold and had court dates. I've done that so many times. And pleading, "Please keep him in the hospital"...I learned if he's not threatening his life or someone else's you can't get him into the hospital.*

Katie used her knowledge of the mental healthcare system to advocate for Kevin's treatment and help him access available resources.

Carmen advocates for her sister, Lily, in times of escalating symptoms related to bipolar disorder. Her advocacy actions are informed by learning about Lily's needs for treatment and resources—understanding her medications, how to access Social Security Disability benefits, and the challenge of finding a psychiatric bed at the hospital. Carmen once took Lily home from the emergency room for monitoring because a psychiatric bed was not available. She also learned about available resources and mental health system policies in three different states where Lily needed services, enabling her to engage in advocacy actions to make sure her sister received care.

Normalizing Mental Illness

Aiming to reduce the stigma and discrimination surrounding mental illness, family members acted as advocates by talking about mental illness and making the topic an acceptable part of everyday conversation. They educated other family members on their relative's experience with mental illness and treatment. In an effort to normalize the experience of mental illness, family members became more open about how coping with a relative's symptoms introduced life challenges. They shared stories describing how their relative learned to advocate for their own needs. They listened and offered support to others who shared experiences with mental illness.

Jessica normalizes mental illness in her work as a public health educator. She offered her perspective on how to communicate care and support when interacting with people who live with a mental illness.

> *Offer as much support as you can. Just be supportive. Don't treat them differently. You don't want to enable them to lean on this disability or use it as an excuse to not live life at its fullest. My mom has shown you can be a successful employee, successful mother, wife, or friend—all those things. You may not be able to be all those things, but you may be able to be one of those things. Maybe being a mother is too much. But maybe you can be a really successful friend, or you can be a really successful worker. You can put all that energy into being a worker. Really support them the way that they need it. Maybe push a little bit, but not so hard that they stop coming to you. Listen well. Pay attention.*

Sam, whose mother completed suicide when he was a teenager, views mental illness as only one of a person's characteristics. He used his mother as an example.

She was my mom who made goulash way too many times every week…Her favorite color was purple. Every spring she would plant some pink flowers and purple flowers. She liked Alfred Hitchcock movies and she had bipolar. So that is how I see the world. [Mental illness] is a characteristic.

Community-Oriented Advocacy

Half of the family members in my study have advocated for disadvantaged populations in work or volunteer roles. Through their advocacy, they have worked with populations living with a mental illness and disabilities, as well as with persons living in long-term care.

In his career as a county mental health social worker, Sam became an advocate for individuals living with a mental illness. He estimates he has served as a caseworker for 1,000 people over the years. He described his approach to meeting with clients.

After we get a little acquainted, I'll ask someone, "What is your diagnosis?" They might say what it is. I'll say, "What does that mean to you?" Most people don't know. Their doctor or therapist will say, "Well, you have schizoaffective or you have bipolar." Then I'll try to educate [them on] what that means, what to watch out for. That these can be symptoms that are heading toward disruption in your life. I see a lot of my work as advocating and educating.

He reflected on how he is using "what was harrowing and so debilitating" at one time in his life to advocate for others through his work.

At a mental health conference, Elaine shared her story about her daughter Terry's suicide attempt. Her decision to share the story was consistent with her advocacy for being open to talking about challenging life experiences. She remarked, "I believe that if you heal something now, it can impact past generations as well as future [ones]. From a spiritual standpoint, if that's the purpose that I'm here for, then I think I've allowed that to take place." In her current work, Elaine advocates for mental health. She teaches classes for an organization that supports complementary healing strategies, participates in meditation retreats, and is excited about how her work helps people.

Participants in my study also advocated through their volunteer work. Three volunteered with the National Alliance on Mental Illness (NAMI), and one served as guardian ad litem to advocate for children's best interests in the courts. Heather, who has both a husband and brother living with a mental illness, engages in advocacy actions that support decisions and policies to improve attention and access to mental healthcare. In her journal, she wrote about her advocacy goals and action steps.

> *Another goal is to advocate for people living with mental illness. This is the goal that I'm most passionate about. This the one that I feel deepest in my soul...I wage my small campaign by sending handwritten thank you notes to people in authority positions for even their small work related to mental health and to magazine editors for including articles or advertisements about mental health...[and] asking city council candidates how they hope to address mental health concerns, or our local hospital board why they're opening a wing for geriatric health rather than mental health.*

Heather's letters to magazine editors on mental health have resulted in two publications, and she has also advocated at NAMI events.

When family members advocate, they contribute to improving mental healthcare for their relative and for others who live with a mental illness. Advocacy empowers the giver and the recipient by giving voice to those without a voice.

CHARACTERISTICS OF ADVOCACY

In mental health, advocates focus on concerns about medications, involuntary detention, insufficient patient information about diagnosis or treatment, and insensitivity from health professionals and caregivers.[5] Inadequate mental healthcare contributes to fearfulness and disempowerment for persons receiving care; advocacy reduces both.

The following list explains key characteristics of advocacy—and what it means to be an effective advocate.[2] Advocacy is:

- *Empowering.* Give individuals the opportunity to speak for themselves. If they are unable, ensure that their view is recognized, understood, and used in decision-making that affects them.
- *Independent.* When advocating, express the individual's views objectively, without bias or prejudice.
- *Inclusive.* Ensure that everyone has the opportunity for access to advocacy.
- *Impartial.* Advocate without judgment and represent the individual's truth.
- *Confidential.* Obtain permission to share information in advocacy actions.
- *Free of cost.* Advocacy activities must be gratuitous.

Advocacy actions for better mental healthcare include: 1) raising awareness about a situation or experience; 2) providing training or education on mental illness, available treatment, and needed policy changes; 3) providing counseling opportunities such as peer support; and 4) mediating situations in which services have been denied.[2]

SELF-ADVOCACY

Self-advocacy "involves people asserting their own rights, expressing their needs and assuming their duties of citizenship to the extent of their capabilities."[4] As a family member, you can advocate for your needs for information and support, and you can also encourage your relative to advocate for themselves. Self-advocacy might seem overwhelming for both you and your relative. You might doubt your own importance, lack confidence to ask for what you need, or want to avoid calling attention to yourself.

Persons who live with mental illness often need to invest significant energy when they are not feeling energetic enough to advocate for themselves. You can facilitate self-advocacy for your relative by encouraging them to take small steps, such as locating needed information or making phone calls, while you support them by walking alongside.

The Wellness Recovery Action Plan (WRAP) website, which provides prevention and wellness tools to promote recovery, offers the following 10 steps for effective self-advocacy.[6] Here, the steps are presented through the lens of how an individual living with a mental illness could use them to self-advocate for a medication change because of distressing side effects. This is just one example of how the steps can be applied. As a family member, you can also apply WRAP's self-advocacy steps to your own needs for supporting your relative.

Ten Steps to Being an Effective Self-Advocate

1. **Believe in yourself.**
   Remember: you are the best judge of what is happening to your body, and you are the expert on what you are feeling.

2. **Know your rights.**
   You have a right to the most effective treatment that does not cause harm to your well-being.

3. **Decide what you want.**
   Although you accept the need to take medication, you also realize you want to be more alert and awake during the day.

4. **Get the facts.**
   Ask people who know you (family members and friends) to share what they are observing about how the medication is affecting you. Ask about the medication dosage you are receiving and how reducing the dosage or changing the medication could affect your symptoms and alertness.

5. **Plan a strategy.**
   Write down your concerns about medication side effects to present to your care provider.

6. Gather support.

Seek peer support by asking others who take medication about strategies they have used to manage their medication.

7. Target efforts.

Focus on how the medication makes you feel and how your body is affected. Determine who you need to consult in order to make a decision about a medication change. Keep a list of your side effects (the side effect, day and time of occurrence, and severity) and ask family and friends to help validate and add to the list.

8. Express yourself clearly.

Follow a written script that lists reasons why you need a medication change. Practice what you plan to say.

9. Assert yourself calmly.

Take a deep breath and focus on your goal.

10. Be firm and persistent.

State that you need time to express your views. Explain how the side effects interfere with your ability to take steps toward recovery. Bring a trusted friend or family member with you to validate your concerns.

Finding the right medication—one that adequately controls symptoms with minimal side effects—is a complex process. Each individual responds differently based on their emotional, cognitive, and physical well-being. Although providers rely on protocol for prescribing medications based on symptoms, finding the right medication and dosage is often a trial-and-error process. Medication management is likely to be more effective when an individual takes an active role in the decision-making process by advocating for their well-being. Following WRAP's 10 steps is one strategy for breaking advocacy into small actions to achieve a goal, such as obtaining mental healthcare that addresses individual needs.

ADVOCATING FOR OTHERS

We can think about advocacy as "empathy in action." Empathy is a precursor to advocacy. We are more likely to advocate for another when we understand their experience. (Refer to Chapter 6 for a refresher on what it means to be empathetic.)

As a family member of an individual living with a mental illness, you can use advocacy strategies to give voice to their needs. Useful advocacy strategies include safeguarding, apprising, valuing, mediating, and championing social justice.[7] Here is a brief overview of each:

> *Safeguarding* involves protecting your relative from potential harm resulting from their symptoms or from treatment that is ineffective or harmful. When harm is suspected, family members call for a crisis response and voice their concerns for their relative.

> *Apprising* means giving truthful and relevant information to your relative about their diagnosis and treatment options. As a family member, seek to collaborate with the mental healthcare team on getting accurate and helpful information for decision-making.

Valuing is about attending to your relative's preferences and choices. Support their autonomy by listening to them and affirming their values and preferences that contribute to their well-being.

Mediating means bringing your relative's needs to the attention of their mental healthcare team. Use this strategy when your relative is not able to or will not give voice to difficulties they are experiencing. Remember, "The squeaky wheel gets the grease."

Championing social justice comes into play when situations are deemed inequitable. Are rules or policies being applied unfairly? Does your relative have access to needed resources? Often, this strategy involves acting at a community level.

Advocacy and Compassion Fatigue

Concern for another, if taken to an extreme, may lead to stress from the emotional burden of wanting to help. As you advocate, watch for signs of compassion fatigue, which may include anxiety, preoccupation, physical symptoms, poor self-care, or exhaustion.[8] Nurturing resilience (see Chapter 8) is a prescription for preventing compassion fatigue. Recognize when you are becoming emotionally and physically exhausted, pay attention to your own self-care, and call in your social support network.

HOW TO ADVOCATE FOR CHANGE IN MENTAL HEALTHCARE

To influence the systems that make decisions about mental healthcare treatment and resources, joining others in advocacy efforts will increase advocacy effectiveness. As you collaborate with others, you will find inspiration, support, and affirmation, and you may also find new friends.

When advocating for others, we often face problems stemming from an inadequate, complex mental healthcare system. The first challenge to overcome is finding out where to start. Who should you talk to? Who will listen? Who is the decision-maker?

Advocacy Example: Mental Health Day

The Hennepin County Local Mental Health Advisory Council in Minnesota advocates for individuals living with serious and persistent mental illness. The Council advises county decision-makers about mental health policy, programs, and services. Council members, appointed by county commissioners, comprise consumers who have received mental health services, family members, mental health providers, at-large members with expertise and special interests in mental health, and a liaison and staff from the county Adult Behavioral Health Services Department.

For two years, Council members joined other mental health organizations on an advocacy project, Mental Health Day at the Minnesota State Fair, to increase awareness about the needs of people who live with a mental illness. The Mental Health Day event presented opportunities to teach the general public about mental illness, programs, and services; normalize mental illness; and, through education, decrease discrimination toward people who seek mental healthcare. Strategies included inviting fairgoers to participate in a mental health trivia wheel game and handing out mental health information.

The following 10-Step Advocacy Framework, offered by World Health Communication Associates and the International Council of Nurses, guides systems-level advocacy strategies.[9] Using the Mental Health Day project as an example, let us consider how the framework can be put into action.

The 10-Step Advocacy Framework

1. Take Action

Overcome obstacles to action. Council members responded to the opportunity to participate in Mental Health Day at the State Fair. They communicated with other mental health organizations, resolved funding needs, and managed busy summer schedules to plan the event.

2. Select Your Issue

Identify and draw attention to an issue. The Council decided to focus on: 1) increasing awareness about mental health issues, and 2) normalizing mental illness by providing facts and information. In recent years, the Council focused on reducing stigma encountered by people who live with a mental illness. Stigma and discrimination prevent people from finding and receiving needed treatment.

3. Understand the Political Context

Identify the key people you need to influence. People who attend the Minnesota State Fair represent urban, suburban, and rural populations of Minnesota and surrounding states. Council members recognized that cultural communication patterns can make it difficult for some to be open about mental illness. They aimed to present the topic in a non-threatening way, framed as a learning opportunity, to help engage the public's interest.

4. **Build Your Evidence Base**

   Do your homework on the issue and map the potential roles of relevant players. Council members found the facts for the trivia wheel on credible mental health organization websites and collaborated with the liaison and staff from the county's Adult Behavioral Health Services to construct and present it.

5. **Engage Others**

   Win the support of key individuals and/or organizations. Event planning included the work of several organizations, including NAMI Minnesota and the Minnesota State Advisory Council on Mental Health. The application for Mental Health Day was approved by the Minnesota State Fair administration. The Hennepin County Mental Health Advisory Council acted as the one local advisory council to partner on the State Fair event along with other mental health organizations.

6. **Develop a Strategic Plan**

   Collectively identify goals and objectives and the best way to achieve them. Planning decisions included identifying the event's location and activities of each organization involved and creating a schedule to maximize public engagement.

7. Communicate Messages and Implement Plans

Deliver your messages and counter the efforts of opposing interest groups. Council members discussed major "talking points" for engaging the public in discussion about mental health issues and needs. In this example, the opposing interest groups could be viewed as all the other State Fair attractions, including food!

8. Seize Opportunities

Time interactions and actions for maximum impact. The schedule placed Council members at the event throughout the day, with greater coverage in the afternoon. Council members interacted with other exhibitors to share information, meet new people, and learn about the services of other organizations.

9. Be Accountable

Monitor and evaluate process and impact. At the Council meeting following the State Fair event, members reviewed the public's response to the advocacy activities. Outcomes of the event, including reactions to the trivia wheel game and distribution of mental health information, were reported to Hennepin County Adult Behavioral Health Services. Also, a local news channel featured a segment about Mental Health Day at the Fair.

10. Take a Developmental Approach

Build sustainable capacity throughout the process. Council members used their experience with the first Mental Health Day at the Fair to plan a repeat performance. They also made adjustments as a result of budget cuts in the county's Human Services and Public Health Department.

In this example, a group accomplished an advocacy activity. Participating in group advocacy efforts is an effective strategy for gaining confidence in your ability to speak up about the experience of people who live with a mental illness and call attention to what is needed to improve their well-being. Examples of other avenues for advocating for system change in mental health services include attending Mental Health Day on the Hill, which provides the opportunity to speak with state representatives and senators about mental health issues. Minnesota's Mental Health Day on the Hill takes place at the state capitol in March and is organized by NAMI Minnesota. Individually, you can advocate at a systems level by writing a letter to your representative or senator, testifying at a hearing on mental health, or supporting organizations that advocate for the needs of people who live with a mental illness.

CHOOSE THE ADVOCACY YOU CAN DO

At this point in your journey, you may not feel ready for advocacy at the systems level. It may be enough for you to advocate for your own self-care and for your relative's needs in the mental healthcare system. Advocacy is about doing what you can do with the energy you have. You are the expert at deciding what is doable for you.

As family members who aspire to support a relative living with a mental illness, we experience crises, overwhelming emotions, and our relative's unpredictability. We learn to cope with difficult and uncertain times. We find acceptance, grow, and become advocates.

In a study of family members whose relatives lived with a persistent and serious mental illness, after a period of dealing with their relative's crises and cycles of instability and stability, the study participants moved into a phase of growth and advocacy.[10] They dedicated time to helping others make the journey through the mental illness maze. Although their concerns about relapses and the future did not go away, many experienced a sense of competence in their ability to give voice to the needs of their relative.

MY ADVOCACY JOURNEY

When I decided to participate in NAMI's Family-to-Family class, I did so with the intent of becoming a class instructor. However, I soon discovered I needed to take some time to muster the energy to move on to teaching. I spent the following year feeling ambivalent about my next steps. I was not ready to jump into teaching others about the journey through the mental illness maze until I reflected further on my new learning on how to better respond to my daughter's symptoms and difficulties. I developed greater confidence in my knowledge about the mental healthcare system and my ability to advocate for good mental healthcare for my daughter. A year later, I completed the Family-to-Family instructor training. I have since co-taught three 12-week classes (now revised to eight weeks); I also became a member of the Hennepin County Adult Mental Health Advisory Council. As I have moved into a larger realm of advocacy, I made new friends and discovered satisfaction in working to create a better world that accepts, nurtures, and encourages people who experience mental illness.

KEY CHAPTER MESSAGES

1. Advocacy involves acting or speaking on behalf of ourselves or others.

2. Mental health advocacy increases awareness about the needs of individuals who live with a mental illness and reduces discrimination.

3. Advocacy actions call attention to the experiences of individuals who live with a mental illness in order to influence decisions that affect them.

4. Family members in the study advocated by giving voice to their relative's needs for mental healthcare and resources, normalizing mental illness, and becoming involved in community activities to communicate the needs of individuals who live with a mental illness.

5. Messages of advocacy should be empowering, objective in communicating perspectives, available to all, impartial without judgment, and shared with permission.

6. Self-advocacy means giving voice to one's own needs and asserting one's rights.

7. WRAP's "Ten Steps to Being an Effective Self-Advocate" offer specific steps that individuals living with a mental illness can take to advocate for their mental healthcare needs and treatment.

8. Five useful advocacy strategies are: safeguarding, apprising, valuing, mediating, and championing social justice.

9. The 10-Step Advocacy Framework, offered by World Health Communication Associates and the International Council of Nurses, is useful for guiding systems-level advocacy actions aimed at improving mental healthcare and resources.

APPENDIX A

QUESTIONS FOR REFLECTION AND SMALL GROUP DISCUSSION

Questions for Parents

1. How did you become aware that your child lives with a mental illness?

2. What were your experiences in interacting with mental healthcare providers and staff in the mental healthcare system?

3. What can you do to communicate your perspectives about your child's symptoms to decision-makers about your child's mental healthcare?

4. How are your family relationships affected by having a child that lives with a mental illness?

5. What do you worry about the most?

6. What strategies have you found that help you to communicate more effectively with your child?

7. How have your expectations or dreams for your child changed?

8. What can you do to find balance between supporting your child and taking care of your own emotional and physical needs?

9. What have you learned about yourself in your search to find help for your child?

10. What does it mean to have realistic hope for your child's recovery?

Questions for Spouses and Partners

1. How did your partner's illness affect your relationship as a couple?

2. How did your partner's illness affect your children?

3. How did you first respond when you realized your partner lives with a mental illness?

4. What did you do to learn more about your partner's diagnosis?

5. What sources of information have been most helpful to you in your search to find resources and/or help for your partner?

6. What boundary- or limit-setting strategies have you used in order to make your life manageable?

7. How have mental health providers and programs been helpful to your partner and to you?

8. What suggestions do you have for how mental health providers and programs could better meet the needs of family members?

9. How has having a partner who lives with a mental illness affected your self-concept?

10. What are your "go-to" coping strategies?

Questions for Siblings

1. How did your sibling's experience with a mental illness affect family relationships?

2. What did you do to support your parents when they first realized one of their children lived with a mental illness?

3. How did having a sibling living with a mental illness affect your own development as a young adult?

4. What did you do to try and help your sibling? What strategies have you found to be helpful? What strategies have not worked?

5. How did your experience with your sibling influence the interactions in your own family?

6. How have mental healthcare professionals and staff facilitated recovery for your sibling?

7. What do you wish could be changed about the mental healthcare system, given your experience as a family member?

8. What are your "go-to" coping strategies for finding balance in supporting your sibling? How do you manage the emotions connected with frustration and disappointment when your sibling's behavior causes difficulty?

9. What strengths do you see in your sibling?

10. How do you balance hope for recovery with acceptance that your sibling lives with a mental illness?

Questions for Adult Children

1. What new understandings do you have about your parent who lives or lived with a mental illness?

2. How has having a parent living with a mental illness affected your life?

3. How do you manage the stress in your life? How have you grown in your ability to manage your stress?

4. How has having a parent living with a mental illness affected your family relationships and other relationships (friends, work)?

5. What support are you getting? What support do you need?

6. How have you changed through your experience of having a parent living with a mental illness?

7. What have you learned to appreciate about your parent who lives or lived with a mental illness?

8. What would you like to see changed in how the healthcare system responds to persons living with a mental illness?

9. What are your thoughts about what you can do to advocate for family members or others who live with a mental illness?

10. What is one thing you would like to change about how you respond to family members who live with a mental illness?

APPENDIX B

STUDY PARTICIPANTS

Parents

The five parents, all college-educated and employed women, have partners or spouses actively involved in co-parenting. Four have young adult children in their 20s who exhibited symptoms of mental illness during the past two to 10 years. One parent's adult child, now in their 40s, has lived with a mental illness for 20 years. Four parents have called a crisis team to their home because of possible harm resulting from their child's behavior.

Partners/Spouses

The partners/spouses, two men and three women, had college (3), technical (1), or high school education (1). One partner was retired, while the other four were employed. The length of time that their family member had exhibited symptoms ranged from three to

40 years. Two partners living with a mental illness had died, one from a car accident (age 66) and the other from cancer (age 71). The three living partners' ages ranged from 47 to 53. Regarding partner relationships, three study participants stayed married, one obtained a divorce, and one cohabited for a lengthy time period before separating from her partner.

Siblings

Sibling participants included one man and four women. All were college educated; three were employed and two were retired. The length of time that their ill sibling exhibited symptoms of a mental illness varied—one for the past eight years, another for the past 23 years, and the remaining three for over 40 years. Ill siblings' ages ranged from 29 to 63.

Adult Children

The five adult children, two men and three women, were all college educated and professionally employed; two were retired. Two of the participants' parents were deceased, one from a completed suicide. All of the parents exhibited symptoms of a mental illness during the childhoods of the adult children.

Summary

Family member participants were predominantly white and had mid-level socioeconomic status. Among the five parents, one was non-white and three parented non-white children. Men comprised 25% of participants. Since many participants in the study enrolled after they learned about the opportunity through the National Alliance on Mental Illness (NAMI), participants represented a population of family members who have actively sought resources for supporting a relative living with a mental illness. Given that many participants in the study were already connected with resources, including NAMI, the study did not capture the experiences of family members who have few financial and emotional resources for supporting a loved one living with a mental illness.

APPENDIX C

INTERVIEW QUESTIONS

I asked study participants the following questions over two interview sessions, a month or more apart. Interviews lasted an average of 1 to 1.5 hours.

1. How did you first realize your family member was experiencing a mental illness?

2. How did you respond to the realization that your family member was living with a mental illness?

3. How is bipolar disorder affecting your family member's life?

4. How has having a family member living with bipolar disorder affected your life?

5. How has having a family member living with bipolar disorder affected your relationships with other family members, with your friends, and your work relationships?

6. What feelings have you experienced connected with having a family member living with bipolar disorder? Describe any feelings of loss or grief that you have experienced.

7. What are sources of strength and/or support that have been helpful to you in adjusting to having a family member living with bipolar disorder?

8. How have your coping strategies changed since you first became aware that your family member was living with bipolar disorder?

9. What burdens or challenges have been especially difficult for you related to having a family member living with bipolar disorder? What is the hardest thing you face daily?

10. How has having a family member living with bipolar disorder affected your view of yourself?

11. What have you learned about yourself in your journey with your family member living with bipolar disorder?

12. How have your interactions with healthcare, mental healthcare, or social services been helpful or not helpful?

13. What challenges has your family member experienced with treatment for bipolar disorder, such as managing medications or other therapies?

14. How does having a family member living with bipolar disorder impact your hopes and dreams for the future?

15. What barriers or obstacles do you encounter that make you feel hesitant in talking to others about your experiences?

16. What good things have come out of your journey with your family member living with bipolar disorder?

17. What advice would you offer to others who have a similar situation?

APPENDIX D

SUGGESTIONS FROM A PARENT (SHARON'S TIPS)

Sharon provided a list of suggestions for supporting an adult child living with bipolar disorder. Sharon's wisdom grew out of her experience of supporting her young adult daughter and her years of providing mental health education in a public health setting. While Sharon's tips are written specifically for parents of young adult children, many also apply to family members of any person living with a mental illness.

- When your young adult child is hospitalized, get them to sign releases for sharing information, even if you never need to use them. (Your child can always rescind.) At the time, you might not think to have them do this. That's where you get into trouble—when you call the hospital the next day and they can't even tell you that your child is in the hospital.
- Respect their decision-making. It's about remembering that they're an adult. They have the right to make the decision.
- Be sure to empower them as much as possible.

- When I believe that my child is making decisions that are not in good judgment, I ask, "Can I offer a different perspective that you could consider?" I think that helps her feel less defensive.
- When an adult child comes back home following hospitalization or a crisis, collaborate with them on changes to their room in order to promote choice and independence.
- To cope, it may help to unfollow them on social media if their posts are scary or make you worry. Let them know you are unfollowing them and why.
- Utilize resources, classes, and groups from the National Alliance on Mental Illness.
- Make friends with others who share your experiences, including parents or people you meet in support groups and classes.
- Seek reliable information from legitimate sources online, such as government agency resources and reputable mental health organizations.
- Avoid online forums, like online parent-to-parent forums, because of misinformation. Look for evidence-based practices and facts.
- Be transparent when talking with providers. Tell your child you are calling their provider to communicate concerns. To avoid breaking drown trust, tell the provider, "You can tell my family member that I called you with this information."
- Screen for suicidal thoughts throughout the recovery process even if your child does not indicate that they have suicidal thoughts. Remove potential means, especially if the person is impulsive.
- For young adults, encourage reliable birth control. Although this may seem awkward, it is not shaming; it helps them to see that now is not the right time for pregnancy.

- Provide positive feedback by sharing examples of good decision-making and new skill development.
- Create a mental illness–free zone: "Today, we are not going to talk about mental illness."
- Create normal rituals. While talking about mental illness or symptoms is important, it should not be in every conversation. We should be able to have dinners and lunches and just play and goof around without mental illness always being a topic.
- Give health systems feedback when care has been less-than-helpful. Don't be afraid to contact the health system.
- Be respectful to the providers at hospitals or clinics. Thank them a lot. Describe how your loved one has benefited from their care. Greet receptionists and other mental health staff who are also part of the mental healthcare team.
- Keep envisioning the future. Identify small steps that lead to recovery.

ENDNOTES

CHAPTER 2

1. BetterHealth Channel, Victoria State Government, Australia. (2020). *Stigma, discrimination and mental illness.* https://www.betterhealth.vic.gov.au/health/servicesandsupport/stigma-discrimination-and-mental-illness
2. Thoits, P. A. (2011). Resisting the stigma of mental illness. *Social Psychology Quarterly, 74*(1) 6-28. doi: 10.1177/0190272511398019
3. Marko-Franks, R. (2016). *Stick it to stigma.* https://www.nami.org/Blogs/NAMI-Blog/November-2016/Stick-It-to-Stigma
4. Corrigan, P. W., & Miller, F. E. (2004). Shame, blame, and contamination: A review of the impact of mental illness stigma on family members. *Journal of Mental Health, 13*(6), 537-548.
5. van der Sanden, R. L. M., Pryor, J. B., Stutterheim, S. B., Kok, G., Bos, A. E. R. (2016). Stigma by association and family burden among family members of people with mental illness: The mediating role of coping. *Social Psychiatry and Psychiatric Epidemiology, 51*, 1233-1245. doi: 10.1007/s00127-016-1256-x

6. Gonzalez-Torres, M. E., Oraa, R., Arıstegui, M., Fernandez-Rivas, A., & Guimon, J. (2007). Stigma and discrimination towards people with schizophrenia and their family members. *Social Psychiatry and Psychiatric Epidemiology, 42,* 14-23. doi: 10.1007/s00127-006-0126-3

7. Mayo Clinic. (2017). *Mental health: Overcoming the stigma of mental illness.* https://www.mayoclinic.org/diseases-conditions/mental-illness/in-depth/mental-health/art-20046477

8. Chen, X., Mao, Y., Kong, L., Li, G., Xin, M., Lou, F., & Ping, Li. (2016). Resilience moderates the association between stigma and psychological distress among family caregivers of patients with schizophrenia. *Personality and Individual Differences, 96,* 78-82.

9. McNally, R. J. (2011). *What is Mental Illness.* Cambridge, MA: The Belknap Press of Harvard University Press.

10. Weir, K. (2012). The roots of mental illness: How much of mental illness can the biology of the brain explain? *Monitor on Psychology, 43*(6), 30. https://www.apa.org/monitor/2012/06/roots

11. National Institute of Mental Health (NIMH). (2019). *Mental health information: Statistics.* https://www.nimh.nih.gov/health/statistics/mental-illness.shtml

12. Mayo Clinic. (2019). *Mental illness.* https://www.mayoclinic.org/diseases-conditions/mental-illness/symptoms-causes/syc-20374968

13. Mental Health America. (2020). *B4Stage4: Changing the way we think about mental health.* https://www.mhanational.org/b4stage4-changing-way-we-think-about-mental-health

14. National Alliance on Mental Illness (NAMI). (2020). *Mental health conditions.* https://www.nami.org/Learn-More/Mental-Health-Conditions

15. American Psychiatric Association. (2020). *What is depression?* https://www.psychiatry.org/patients-families/depression/what-is-depression

16. Centers for Disease Control and Prevention (CDC). (2018). *Learn about mental health.* https://www.cdc.gov/mentalhealth/learn/

17. Heinssen, R. K., Goldstein, A. B., Azrin, S. T. (2014). *Evidence-based treatments for first episode psychosis: Components of coordinated specialty care.* National Institute of Mental Health. https://www.nimh.nih.gov/health/topics/schizophrenia/raise/nimh-white-paper-csc-for-fep_147096.pdf

18. National Institute of Mental Health (NIMH). (2015). *Fact sheet: First episode psychosis.* https://www.nimh.nih.gov/health/topics/schizophrenia/raise/fact-sheet-first-episode-psychosis.shtml

19. National Alliance on Mental Illness (NAMI). (2020). *Crisis intervention team (CIT) programs.* https://nami.org/Advocacy/Crisis-Intervention/Crisis-Intervention-Team-(CIT)-Programs

20. Substance Abuse and Mental Health Services Administration. (2019). *Workforce.* https://www.samhsa.gov/workforce

21. Mayo Clinic. (2019a). *Electroconvulsive therapy (ECT).* https://www.mayoclinic.org/tests-procedures/electroconvulsive-therapy/about/pac-20393894

22. Mayo Clinic. (2020). *Transcranial magnetic stimulation.* https://www.mayoclinic.org/tests-procedures/transcranial-magnetic-stimulation/about/pac-20384625

CHAPTER 3

1. Schnitker, S. A. (2012). An examination of patience and well-being. *The Journal of Positive Psychology, 7*(4), 263-280. doi.org/10.1080/17439760.2012.697185

2. National Alliance on Mental Illness. (2020). *Predictable emotional responses.* NAMI Family-to-Family Education Program.

3. DiGiulio, S. (2019). *How to train yourself to be more patient.* NBC News. https://www.nbcnews.com/better/lifestyle/how-train-yourself-be-more-patient-ncna1022356

4. Brainy Quotes (2019). *Top 10 patience quotes.* https://www.brainyquote.com/lists/topics/top-10-patience-quotes

CHAPTER 4

1. Tartakovsky, M. (2018b). *How to relinquish unrealistic expectations.* Psychcentral.com. https://psychcentral.com/lib/how-to-relinquish-unrealistic-expectations/

2. Roese, N. J., & Sherman, J. W. (2007). Expectancy. In A. W. Kruglanski, E. T. Higgins, *Social psychology: Handbook of basic principles (pp. 91-115).* New York: The Guilford Press.

3. Stout, E. (2019). *The expectations vs. reality trap: Are you being robbed of your happiness?* Verywellmind.com. https://www.verywellmind.com/expectation-vs-reality-trap-4570968

4. Tartakovsky, M. *5 suggestions for setting realistic expectations for yourself.* Psychcentral.com. https://psychcentral.com/blog/5-suggestions-for-setting-realistic-expectations-with-yourself/

5. Agathangelou, F. (2014). *How to stop expecting too much from yourself.* HealthyPlace.com. https://www.healthyplace.com/blogs/buildingselfesteem/2015/07/do-you-expect-too-much-from-yourself

CHAPTER 5

1. Scott, E. (2020). *How to reframe situations so they create less stress.* https://www.verywellmind.com/cognitive-reframing-for-stress-management-3144872
2. Robson, J. P., & Troutman-Jordan, M. (2014). A concept analysis of cognitive reframing. *The Journal of Theory Construction and Testing, 18*(2), 55-59.
3. Smith, G., Gregory, K., & Higgs, A. (2007). *An integrated approach to family work for psychosis: A manual for family workers.* Philadelphia: Jessica Kingsley Publishers.
4. Scott, E. (2020). *Cognitive distortions and stress.* https://www.verywellmind.com/cognitive-distortions-and-stress-3144921
5. Scott, E. (2020). *Explanatory styles and their role in stress.* https://www.verywellmind.com/about-explanatory-styles-3145110

CHAPTER 6

1. Krznaric, R. (2014). *Empathy: Why it Matters, and How You Get It.* New York: Perigee, preface.
2. Riess, H. (2018). *The empathy effect.* Boulder, CO: Sounds True.
3. National Alliance on Mental Illness. (2020a). *NAMI Family-to-Family Curriculum.* Worksheet 1: Empathy.
4. National Alliance on Mental Illness. (2020b). *NAMI Family-to-Family Curriculum.* Worksheet 6: Guidelines for offering empathy, p. 7.26.

5. Ness, N., Borg, M., Semb, R., & Karlsson, B. (2014). "Walking alongside:" collaborative practices in mental health and substance use care. *International Journal of Mental Health Systems, 8*, 1-8. http://www.ijmhs.com/content/8/1/55

CHAPTER 7

1. Mayo Clinic. (2020). *Social support: Tap this tool to beat stress.* https://www.mayoclinic.org/healthy-lifestyle/stress-management/in-depth/social-support/art-20044445
2. National Cancer Institute. (2020). *Definition: Social support.* https://www.cancer.gov
3. Schaffer, M. A. (2017). Social support. In S. J. Peterson & T. S. Bredow (Eds.) *Middle range theories: Application to nursing research* (pp. 117-135). Philadelphia: Wolters Kluwer.
4. Ozbay, F., Johnson, D. C., Dimoulas, E., Morgan III, C. A., Charney, D., & Southwick, S. (2007). Social support and resilience to stress: From neurobiology to clinical practice. *Psychiatry, 4*(5), 35-40.
5. Bademili, K., & Duman, C. C. (2014). Effects of a Family-to-Family Support Program on the mental health and coping strategies of caregivers of adults with mental illness: A randomized controlled study. *Archives of Psychiatric Nursing, 28*, 392-398. doi.org/10.1016/j.apnu.2014.08.011
6. Chen, F., & Greenberg, J. S. (2004). A positive aspect of caregiving: The influence of social support on caregiving gains for family members of relatives with schizophrenia. *Community Mental Health Journal, 40*(5), 423-435.
7. Pernice-Duca, F., Biegel, D. E., Hess, H. R., Chung, C., & Chang, C. (2015). Family members' perceptions of how

they benefit when relatives living with serious mental illness participate in clubhouse community programs. *Family Relations, 64*, 446-459. doi: 10.1111/fare.12127

8. American Psychological Association. (2020). *Manage stress: Strengthen your social support network.* https://www.apa.org/helpcenter/emotional-support

CHAPTER 8

1. American Psychological Association. (2020). *Building your resilience.* https://www.apa.org/topics/resilience
2. Southwick, S. M., & Charney, D. S. (2012). *Resilience: The science of mastering life's greatest challenges.* Cambridge, UK: Cambridge University Press.
3. Lachman, V. D. (2016). Moral resilience: Managing and preventing moral residue and moral distress. *MedSurg Nursing 25*(2), 121-124.
4. Whittington, B. L., & Scher, S. J. (2010). Prayer and subjective well-being: An examination of six different types of prayer. *The International Journal for the Psychology of Religion, 20*, 59-68. doi: 10.1080/10508610903146316
5. Power, J., Goodyear, M., Maybery, D., Reupert, A., O'Hanlon, B., Cuff, R., & Perlesz, A. (2016). Family resilience in families where a parent has a mental illness. *Journal of Social Work, 16*(1), 66-82. doi: 10.1177/1468017314568081
6. Horner, G., (2016). Resilience. *Journal of Pediatric Health Care, 31*(3), 384-390. doi: 10.1016.j.pedhc.2016.09
7. Mayo Clinic. (2020). *Resilience: Build skills to endure hardship.* https://www.mayoclinic.org/tests-procedures/resilience-training/in-depth/resilience/art-20046311

CHAPTER 9

1. Downman, T. H. (2008). Hope and hopelessness: Theory and reality. *Journal of the Royal Society, 101*, 428-430, p. 248. doi: 10.1258/jrsm.2008.080193
2. Jon Pederson, *"Do you see?"* Sermon notes, December 2, 2018.
3. Park, J., & Chen, R. K. (2016). Positive psychology and hope as a means to recovery from mental illness. *Journal of Applied Rehabilitation Counseling, 47*(2), 34-42.
4. Werner, S. (2012). Subjective well-being, hope, and needs of individuals with serious mental illness. *Psychiatric Research, 196*, 214-219. doi: 10.1016/psychres.2011.10.012
5. Hellman, C. M., Worley, J. A., & Munoz, R. T. (2018). Hope as a coping resource for caregiver resilience and well-being (pp 81-98). In Bailey, W. A. & Harrist, A. W. (Eds.). *Family caregiving: Fostering resilience across the life course.* Cham, Switzerland: Springer.
6. Duggleby, W., Holtslander, L., Kylma, J., Duncan, V., Hammond, C., & Williams, A. (2010). Metasynthesis of the hope experience of family caregivers of persons with chronic illness. *Qualitative Health Research, 20*(2), 148-158. doi: 10.1177/1049732309358239
7. Bland, R., & Darlington, Y. (2002). The nature and sources of hope: Perspectives of family caregivers of people with serious mental illness. *Perspectives in Psychiatric Care, 38*(2), 61-68.
8. Schrank, B., Bird, V., Rudnick, A., & Slade, M. (2012). Determinants, self-management strategies and interventions for hope in people with mental disorders: Systematic search

and narrative review. *Social Science and Medicine, 74*, 554-564. doi:10.1016/j.socscimed.2011.11.008

CHAPTER 10

1. Substance Abuse and Mental Health Services Administration. (2019). *Recovery and recovery support.* **https://www.samhsa.gov/find-help/recovery**
2. Schrank, B., & Slade, M. (2007). Recovery in psychiatry. *Psychiatric Bulletin, 31*, 321-325. doi: 10.1192/pb.bp106.01342
3. Slade, M. (2010). Mental illness and well-being: The central importance of positive psychology and recovery approaches. *BMC Health Services Research, 10*:1-14. **http://www.biomedcentral.com/1472-6963/10/26**
4. Leamy, M., Bird, C., Le Boutillier, C., Williams, J., & Slade, M. (2011). Conceptual framework for personal recovery in mental health: Systematic review and narrative synthesis. *The British Journal of Psychiatry, 199*, 445-452. doi: 10.1192/bjp.bp.110.083733
5. Van Weeghel, J., van Zelst, C., Boertien, D., & Hasson-Ohayon, I., (2019). Conceptualizations, assessments, and implications of personal recovery in mental illness: A scoping review of systematic reviews and meta-analyses. *Psychiatric Rehabilitation Journal, 42*(2), 169-181. doi.org/10.1037.prj0000356
6. Wyder, M., & Bland, R. (2014). The recovery framework as a way of understanding families' response to mental illness: Balancing different needs and recovery journeys. *Australian Social Work, 67*(2), 179-196. doi.org/10.1080/0312407X.2013.875580

7. Slade, M., Amering, M., Farkas, M., Hamilton, B., O'Hagan, M., Panther, G., Perkins, R., Shepherd, G., Tse, S., & Whitley, R. (2014). Use and abuses of recovery: Implementing recovery-oriented practices in mental health systems. *World Psychiatry, 13*, 12-20. doi: 10.1002/wps.20084

8. Piat, M., Sabetti, J., Fleury, M., Boyer, R., & Lesage, A. (2011). "Who believes most in me and in my recovery": The importance of families for persons with serious mental illness living in structured community housing. *Journal of Social Work in Disability & Rehabilitation, 10*(1), 49-65. doi: 10.1080/1536710X.2011.546310

9. Aldersey, H. M., & Whitley, R. (2015). Family influence in recovery from severe mental illness. *Community Mental Health Journal, 51*, 467-476. doi: 10.1007/s10597-014-9783-y

10. Fox, J., Ramon, S., & Morant, N. (2015). Exploring the meaning of recovery for carers: Implications for social work practice. *British Journal of Social Work, 45*, Supplement 1, 117-134. doi: 10.1093/bjsw/bcv109

11. Mallinson, R. L., & Walton-Moss, B. A. (2002). Families of patients with mental illness revised their ideas of what it means to live a "normal" life. *Western Journal of Nursing Research, 24*, 516-536.

12. Park, J., & Chen, R. K. (2016). Positive psychology and hope as means to recovery from mental illness. *Journal of Applied Rehabilitation Counseling, 47*(2), 34-42, p. 34.

13. American Psychological Association. (2017). *What is cognitive behavioral therapy?* https://www.apa.org/ptsd-guideline/patients-and-families/cognitive-behavioral

14. Psychology Today. (2021). *Dialectical Behavior Therapy.* https://www.psychologytoday.com/us/therapy-types/dialectical-behavior-therapy

15. Slade, M. (2010). Mental illness and well-being: The central importance of positive psychology and recovery approaches. *BMC Health Services Research, 10*:1-14. **http://www.biomed-central.com/1472-6963/10/26**

16. National Alliance on Mental Illness. (2020). *Class 7. Worksheet 9: Recovery defined.* NAMI Family-to-Family, 6th edition.

17. National Alliance on Mental Illness. (2020). *Class 5. Worksheet 18: Warning signs of relapse.* NAMI Family-to-Family, 6th edition.

18. National Alliance on Mental Illness. (2020). *Class 7. Worksheet 15: Innovative recovery approaches.* NAMI Family-to-Family, 6th edition.

19. National Alliance on Mental Illness. (2020). *Class 7. Worksheet 8: An open letter to families.* NAMI Family-to-Family, 6th edition.

CHAPTER 11

1. Michael, R. (2018). *What self-care is—and what it isn't.* PsychCentral. **https://psychcentral.com/blog/what-self-care-is-and-what-it-isnt-2/**

2. Barrata, M. (2018). *Self-care 101.* **https://www.psychology-today.com/us/blog/skinny-revisited/201805/self-care-101**

3. Davis, T. (2018). *Self-care: Twelve ways to take better care of yourself.* **https://www.psychologyto-day.com/us/blog/click-here-happiness/201812/self-care-12-ways-take-better-care-yourself**

4. National Alliance on Mental Illness. (2020). *Taking care of yourself.* **https://www.nami.org/Find-Support/Family-Members-and-Caregivers/Taking-Care-of-Yourself**

5. National Alliance on Mental Illness. (2008). *Self-care inventory.* https://nami.org/getattachment/extranet/education,-training-and-outreach-programs/signature-classes/nami-homefront/hf-additional-resources/hf15ar6selfcare.pdf

6. Princeton University. (2020). *Wellness wheel & assessment.* https://umatter.princeton.edu/action-matters/caring-yourself/wellness-wheel-assessment

7. Substance Abuse and Mental Health Services Administration. (2016). *Creating a healthier life: A step-by-step guide to wellness.* https://store.samhsa.gov/sites/default/files/d7/priv/sma16-4958.pdf

8. Minnesota Department of Health. (2019). *Public health interventions: Applications for public health nursing practice.* (2nd ed). https://www.health.state.mn.us/communities/practice/research/phncouncil/wheel.html

9. Foote, J., Wilkens, C., & Kosanke, N. (2014). *Beyond addiction: How science and kindness help people change.* New York: Scribner.

CHAPTER 12

1. PsychU. (2019). *Giving mental illness a voice: Patient perspectives on self-disclosure & stigma.* Webinar, May 23, 2019. https://www.psychu.org/giving-mental-illness-a-voice-patient-perspectives-on-self-disclosure-stigma/

2. Varghese, J. P. (2015). Advocacy in mental health: Giving voice to the voiceless. *Indian Journal of Social Psychiatry, 31,* 4-8.

3. Wisconsin Coalition for Advocacy. (2005). *Advocacy tool kit skills for effective self and peer advocacy.* http://www.

disabilityrightswi.org/wp-content/uploads/2018/04/Advocacy-Tool-Kit.pdf

4. Jugessur, T., & Iles, I. K. (2009). Advocacy in mental health nursing: An integrative review of the literature. *Journal of Psychiatric and Mental Health Nursing, 16*, 187-195, p. 186,189.

5. Stomski, N. J., Morrison, P., Whitely, M., & Brennan, P. (2018). Mental health consumers' motives for seeking advocacy support: A qualitative exploration. *Community Mental Health Journal, 54*, 607-615. doi: 10.1007/s10597-017-0177-9

6. Wellness Recovery Action Plan. (2018). *How to self-advocate.* https://mentalhealthrecovery.com/info-center/how-to-self-advocate/

7. Abbasinia, M., Ahmadi, F., & Kazemnejad, A. (2020). Patient advocacy in nursing: A concept analysis. *Nursing Ethics, 27*(1), 141-151. doi: 10.1177/0969733019832950

8. Gentry, E. (2018). Fighting compassion fatigue and burnout by building emotional resilience. *Journal of Oncology Navigation and Survivorship, 2*(12), 532-535.

9. World Health Communication Association. (2010). *Promoting health: Advocacy guide for health professionals.* http://www.comminit.com/global/content/promoting-health-advocacy-guide-health-professionals

10. Muhlbauer, S. A. (2002). Navigating the storm of mental illness: Phases in the family's journey. *Qualitative Health Research, 12*(8), 1076-1092. doi: 10/1177/10497302236576

ACKNOWLEDGMENTS

I am immensely grateful for friends who have helped me navigate the sadness, grief, and hope I encountered in my efforts to find help for my daughter, who lives with bipolar disorder. Thank you to Carol, Greg, Juanita, Lee, Linda, and Pamela, who joined me in the National Alliance on Mental Illness (NAMI) class that inspired me to write this book, and to Cathy, who co-taught NAMI Family-to-Family classes with me. Karen, Dan, Dennis, and Winnie, who are members of my book club, listened to the stories my husband and I shared over the years about our journey to find help in a complex mental healthcare system.

The many tools and resources provided by NAMI made it possible for me to understand my daughter's experience and move toward acceptance and hope for recovery. Thank you to my writing group, Phyllis, Renée, and Linda, who provided suggestions for improving my writing and championed my progress. My husband has been a continuous staunch supporter of my research on family stories and over the years has partnered with me in the search for effective resources and treatment to help our daughter.

The Chi-at-Large Chapter of Sigma Theta Tau International Honor Society of Nursing awarded me a grant to conduct the research interviews, making it possible to provide participants with a small honorarium. Thank you to NAMI Minnesota for featuring a newsletter article on my study, resulting in many family members contacting me about sharing their stories. I am thankful for the Hennepin County Library system, which provided space where I met many of the study participants who shared their stories.

Thank you to Linda Atwood, Steve Bjerke, Juanita Jensen, and Carol Webster, who each read the next-to-final draft of this book and whose insightful suggestions led to changes to improve reader experience. Finally, I am grateful to the courageous family members who participated in my study. They have given us a gift in sharing with us their stories.

ABOUT THE AUTHOR

Dr. Marjorie Schaffer, Ph.D., R.N., Professor of Nursing Emerita, taught public health nursing at Bethel University in St. Paul, Minnesota, for 31 years. At Bethel, she taught public health nursing and nursing research and developed expertise in qualitative research. She has authored two nursing textbooks and over 50 professional journal articles. She has worked in public health nursing and psychiatric nursing and holds a doctorate in Family Social Science. As a Fulbright Scholar and Specialist, Dr. Schaffer traveled to Norway and New Zealand for research, consultation, and teaching. Her experience with parenting an adult daughter living with bipolar disorder led to exploring how mental illness affects families. Dr. Schaffer has volunteered with the National Alliance on Mental Illness, teaching Family-to-Family classes; served on the Hennepin County Adult Mental Health Advisory Council; and volunteered as an ambassador with Mental Health Connect at her church.

Related professional articles:

- Schaffer, M. A. (2020). Family perspectives of healthcare for relatives living with a mental illness. *Perspectives in Psychiatric Care*, 1-11. **https://doi.org/10.1111/ppc.12718**
- Schaffer, M.A. (2021). **Speaking up: How family members advocate for relatives living with a mental illness.** *Community Mental Health Journal.* **https://doi.org/10.1007/s10597-021-00775-z**

To find more information on Dr. Schaffer's expertise and research on family members who have a loved one living with a mental illness, visit **https://www.familybipolarstories.com.**

Made in the USA
Monee, IL
05 June 2021